PHYSICAL GEOGRAPHY

ABOUT THE AUTHOR

Ross Norton Pearson is Professor of Geography in the College of Literature, Science and the Arts at the University of Michigan. He received the degrees of B.Ed. from Illinois State Normal University, M.S. from the University of Wisconsin, and Ph.D. from the University of Michigan. Professor Pearson has also taught at Eastern Michigan University, San Diego State College, and the University of Colorado.

Professor Pearson is a member of the Executive Board of the National Council for Geographic Education, and holds membership in the Association of American Geographers, the American Geographical Society, and the Michigan Academy of Arts, Science and Letters. He has been a member of the National Research Council Advisory Committee to the Department of State for the Pan American Institute of Geography and History since 1960; was Consultant to the International Development Service and International Cooperation Administration on Agricultural Colonization in Guatemala in 1960; served as Delegate to the Seventh General Assembly of the Pan American Institute of Geography and History at Buenos Aires in 1961; and has been Chairman of the Working Group on Population Mapping of the Pan American Institute of Geography and History since 1961. He is currently Associate Director of the Organization for Tropical Studies. Professor Pearson has written several articles for scholarly journals in the United States and Latin America.

Physical Geography

ROSS NORTON PEARSON

Professor of Geography

University of Michigan

BARNES & NOBLE, Inc.   NEW YORK

Publishers   Booksellers   Since 1873

Preface

This outline is designed for use in connection with courses in introductory physical geography, earth science, and general geography. The organization is similar to that of most such courses. A key to standard textbooks is provided and a reference list of more advanced reading sources is given at the end of each chapter. The book may be used as a syllabus in courses which have comprehensive lectures or as a supplement to standard textbooks. Advanced students who wish to review the basic principles of physical geography will also find it helpful.

The field of physical geography is so broad that no one person can be as competent as he would like to be in all aspects of the subject. The ideas for a book of this scope were of necessity derived from a variety of sources over a period of more than twenty-five years. A great many of them came from my two major professors in each of the three universities which I had the privilege of attending. Harry Lathrop and Leslie Holmes of the (then) Illinois State Normal University provided the stimulation which attracted me to geography and a basic background in the subject. Vernor Finch and Glenn Trewartha of the University of Wisconsin introduced me to the rigors of graduate work and supervised my first efforts as a college teacher. Kenneth McMurry and Charles Davis of the University of Michigan supplied me with a philosophical background of geography and many practical applications of the subject. I am deeply grateful for the guidance of my mentors and apologize to them for the errors and overgeneralizations which will undoubtedly be found on these pages. They are my responsibility, not theirs.

The content of this book has also been greatly influenced by the students who have taken geography courses with me over the years. Their reactions to what has been written in textbooks, and to my own presentations, have often determined the viewpoint that has been taken on many topics in this book, as well as what subjects have been included or omitted. Without this experience gained in working with my students, the book could not have been written.

I am grateful to George Philip and Son Limited for permission to use the Philip drawing of the interrupted Mollweide projection as the basis for the world maps prepared for this volume. Finally, I want to express my appreciation to the Editorial Department of Barnes & Noble, Inc., particularly to Mary Johnson and Joan Smyth, for their assistance in the preparation of this outline. All have been very helpful and have endured my shortcomings with admirable patience.

Ross Norton Pearson
Ann Arbor, Michigan
1967

Contents

	Tabulated Bibliography of Standard Textbooks	viii
	Quick Reference Table to Standard Textbooks	xiii
1	The Field of Geography	1
2	The Planet Earth	8
3	Climatic Controls and Climatic Elements	30
4	Climatic Types	54
5	The Origins of Surface Features	84
6	Major Types of Landforms	103
7	Natural Vegetation	125
8	Soils	136
9	Water Resources	146
10	The Oceans and Seas	164
11	The Fuel Minerals	180
12	The Metallic Minerals	197
13	Physical Geography in Perspective	214
	Glossary	219
	Index	231

World Maps

World Types of Climate	56
World Landform Types	108
World Natural Vegetation Types	126
World Soil Types	140

TABULATED BIBLIOGRAPHY OF STANDARD TEXTBOOKS

This *College Outline* is keyed to standard textbooks in two ways.

1. If you are studying one of the following textbooks, consult the cross references here listed to find which pages of the *Outline* summarize the appropriate chapter of your text. (Roman numerals refer to the textbook chapters, Arabic figures to the corresponding *Outline* pages.)

2. If you are using the *Outline* as your basis for study and need a fuller treatment of a topic, consult the pages of any of the standard textbooks as indicated in the Quick Reference Table on pages xiii-xiv.

Freeman, Otis W., and Raup, H. F., *Essentials of Geography.* 2nd ed. New York: McGraw-Hill, 1959.
I (1-7); II (8-29); III (31-35, 49-52); IV (35-49); V (54-57, 125-128); VI (57-64); VII (64-67); VIII (67-71); IX (71-76); X (76-80); XI (125-134); XII (84-101); XIII (103-105, 111-117, 120-123); XIV (103-111, 117-120); XV (164-175); XVI (175-179); XVII (136-144); XIX (180-213); XX (146-163).

Griffin, Paul F., and Chatham, Ronald L., *Introductory College Geography.* San Francisco: Fearon, 1965.
I (8-29); II (164-179); III (84-101, 103-123); IV (136-144, 125-134, 146-163); V (30-52); VI (57-62); VII (62-64); VIII (60-62); IX (64-67); X (80-83, 110-111); XI (67-69); XII (69-71); XIII (73-75); XIV (75-76); XV (64-67); XVI (71-73); XVII (80-83, 110-111); XVIII (76-78); XIX (78-80); XX (78-80).

Heintzelman, Oliver H., and Highsmith, Richard M., Jr., *World Regional Geography.* 3rd ed. Englewood Cliffs, N. J.: Prentice-Hall, 1967.

I (1-7, 12-29); III (214-218); VI (54-57); VII (57-62); VIII (62-64); X (64-66); XI (80-83, 110-111, 134); XII (67-69); XIII (69-71); XIV (73-75); XV (75-76); XVI (64-67); XVII (71-73); XVIII (80-83, 110-111, 134); XIX (76-78); XX (78-80).

Hoyt, Joseph B., *Man and the Earth.* 2nd ed. Englewood Cliffs, N. J.: Prentice-Hall, 1967.

II (216-218); III (8-12, 164-165); IV (84-123); V (30-53); VI (54-57); VII (146-163, 164-173); VIII (125-135); IX (136-145); X (180-213); XI (57-64); XII (64-69); XIII (76-80); XIV (67-76); XVI (3-7, 214-218); Appendix (17-29).

James, Preston E., *A Geography of Man.* 3rd ed. Waltham, Mass.: Blaisdell, 1966.

Introd. (67, 109-110, 54-57, 125, 139-141, 214-216, 4-7, 216-218); Group I (64-69, 133-134, 92, 99-100, 120-123); Group II (57-62, 128-130, 141-142); Group III (62-64, 132); Group IV (67-69, 100); Group V (69-76, 130-131, 92-95, 111-120, 141-142); Group VI (66-67, 138-139, 142-143); Group VII (76-78, 95-99, 114-116, 142); Group VIII (78-80, 133-134, 144); Group IX (80-83, 105-111, 134); Conclusion (214-218); Appendix A (17-29); Appendix B (30-53, 54-57); Appendix C (84-102); Appendix D (146-163, 164-179); Appendix E (125-135).

Kendall, Henry M., Glendinning, Robert M., and MacFadden, Clifford H., *Introduction to Geography.* 4th ed. New York: Harcourt, Brace & World, 1967.

I (1-7); II (8-17); III (17-29); IV (146-163); V (84-91); VI (91-101); VII (103-123); VIII (30-49); IX (49-53); X (54-67); XI (67-83); XII (136-145); XIII (125-135); XIV (214-218); XXII (180-196); XXIII (197-213).

McIntyre, Michael P., *Physical Geography.* New York: Ronald, 1966.

I (8-17); II (17-29); III (30-53); IV (54-83); V (125-135); VI (136-145); VII (84-101); VIII (146-163); IX (164-179).

Meyer, Alfred H., and Strietelmeier, John H., *Geography in World Society*. Philadelphia: Lippincott, 1963.
I (1-7); V (8-17, 64-65, 175-176); VI (30, 54-57); VII (103-123); VIII (136-145); IX (146-163); X (125-135); XI (180-213); XIX (78-80, 133-134); XX (64-66, 133); XXI (66-67, 132-133, 142-144); XXII (62-64, 131-132); XXIII (57-62, 128-129, 141-142); XXIV (67-69, 130); XXV (69-71, 130-132, 141-142); XXVI (71-73, 131); XXVII (76-78, 131, 142); XXVIII (75-76, 131, 142-143); XXIX (73-75, 132, 142-143); XXXV (214-218).

Miller, E. Willard, and Langdon, George, *Exploring Earth Environments: A World Geography*. New York: Crowell, 1964.
Introd. (1-7); I (8-29); II (30-53); III (54-83); IV (84-102); V (103-124); VI (136-145); VII (164-179); VIII (146-163); XI (180-213).

Murphey, Rhoads, *An Introduction to Geography*. 2nd ed. Chicago: Rand McNally, 1966.
I (1-5, 6); III (214-216); VI (30-53); VII (125-135); VIII (136-145); IX (146-163); X (84-124); XI (217-218).

Powers, William E., *Physical Geography*. New York: Appleton-Century-Crofts, 1966.
I (1-7); II (84-86); III (86-91); IV (91-92); V (92-93); VI (93-95, 114); VII (106, 118-119); VIII (99-100); IX (100); X (95-98, 115); XI (95, 98-99, 105-111); XII (100-101, 176-179); XXII (30-31); XXIII (8-12, 31-32); XXIV (33, 49); XXV (35, 51-52); XXVI (35-41); XXVII (47-48); XXVIII (49-51); XXIX (29); XXX (40-47); XXXI (47); XXXII (54-57); XXXIII (57-64); XXXIV (64-67); XXXV (67-69); XXXVI (69-71); XXXVII (71-73); XXXVIII (73-76); XXXIX (64-67); XL (76-83); XLIII (180-196); XLIV (197-198); XLV (198-204); XLVI (204-206); XLVII (206-212); L (146-155); LI (155-156); LII (157-158); LIII (158-159); LIV (136-145); LVI (125-135).

Shaw, Earl B., *Fundamentals of Geography*. New York: Wiley, 1965.
I (1-7, 214-218); II (8-29); III (30); IV (30-53); V (84-102); VI (103-124); VII (164-179); VIII (146-163); IX (125-135); X (136-145); XI (180-213); XII (54-64); XIII (64-67); XIV (67-71); XV (71-76); XVI (76-80).

Strahler, Arthur N., *Introduction to Physical Geography*. New York: Wiley, 1965.

I (12-29); II (12-14, 16-17, 31-33); III (8-12, 30-33, 48, 49); IV (35-40, 51-52); V (49-51); VI (40-47); VII (54-57); VIII (146-151); IX (57-67); X (67-76); XI (76-83); XII (136-141); XIII (141-145); XIV (125-128); XV (128-135); XVI (85-86); XVII (84-85); XVIII (91-92); XIX (149-153); XX (92-95, 114-115); XXII (95-99, 115); XXIII (100-101, 176-179); XXIV (99-100); XXV (112, 114, 118-119); XXVI (87-89, 106-107); XXVII (89-91, 107-109).

Strahler, Arthur N., *Physical Geography*. 2nd ed. New York: Wiley, 1960.

Introd. (1-7); I (8); II (19-25); III (12); IV (8-14); V (14-16); VI (169-171); VII (30-33, 49); VIII (35-40, 51-52); IX (47-48, 171-173); X (49-51); XI (40-47); XII (54-57); XIII (57-67); XIV (67-76); XV (76-83); XVI (136-141); XVII (141-145); XVIII (103-105); XIX (84-86); XX (84-85); XXI (149-151, 100); XXII (91-92); XXIII (92-93, 151-153); XXIV (93-95); XXVI (95-99, 115); XXVII (100-101); XXVIII (99-100); XXIX (112-113, 114, 118); XXX (106-107); XXXI (107-109).

Trewartha, Glenn T., Robinson, Arthur H., and Hammond, Edwin H., *Elements of Geography*. 5th ed. New York: McGraw-Hill, 1967.

I (8-17); II (17-29); III (30-33, 48, 49); IV (33-40, 51-53); V (49-51); VI (40-47); VII (54-64); VIII (64-67); IX (67-73); X (73-78); XI (78-83); XII (84-91); XIII (91-101); XIV (103-105); XV (111-117); XVI (105-111, 117-120); XVII (120-123); XVIII (173-179); XIX (164-173); XX (146-163); XXI (125-135); XXII (136-141); XXIII (141-145); XXIV (180-213).

Trewartha, Glenn T., Robinson, Arthur H., and Hammond, Edwin H., *Physical Elements of Geography*. 5th ed. New York: McGraw-Hill, 1967.

I (8-17); II (17-29); III (30-33, 48, 49); IV (33-40, 51-53); V (49-51); VI (40-47); VII (54-64); VIII (64-67); IX (67-73); X (73-78); XI (78-83); XII (84-91); XIII (91-101); XIV (103-105); XV (111-117); XVI (105-111, 117-120); XVII (120-123); XVIII (173-179); XIX (164-173); XX (146-163); XXI (125-135); XXII (136-141); XXIII (141-145); XXIV (180-213).

Van Riper, Joseph E., *Man's Physical World*. New York: McGraw-Hill, 1962.

I (1-7, 214-218); II (8-29); III (86-101, 112-115, 107-109); IV (103-123); V (48, 84-86, 99-100); VI (30-35, 47-51); VII (35-47, 51-52); VIII (54-83); IX (125-128); X (128-135); XI (136-141); XII (141-145); XIII (180-213); XIV (146-163); XV (164-179).

White, C. Langdon, and Renner, George T., *College Geography*. New York: Appleton-Century-Crofts, 1957.

III (30-52); IV (57-62); V (64-66); VI (62-64); VII (66-67); VIII (67-69); IX (69-71); X (67-69); XI (73-76); XII (66-67); XIII (71-73); XIV (76-78); XV (78-80); XVI (125-134); XIX (86-89, 91-101); XX (111-117); XXI (105-111); XXII (117-120); XXIII (120-123); XXIV-XXV (136-144); XXVI (180-181, 84-86, 197-198); XXVIII (197-213); XXIX (180-195); XXX (149-151); XXXI (151-159); XXXII (164-179); XXXV (1-3, 8-29); XXXVIII (3-7, 214-218).

QUICK REFERENCE TABLE TO STANDARD TEXTBOOKS

All figures refer to pages. See pages viii to xii for complete titles.

Chapter in this Outline	Topic	Freeman & Raup	Griffin & Chatham	Heintzelman & Highsmith	Hoyt	James	Kendall et al.	McIntyre	Meyer & Strietelmeier	Miller & Langdon
1	The Field of Geography	1–8	xiii–xiv	1–10	57–58	vii–ix 3–6	3–13	3–59	2–25	1–5
2	The Planet Earth	9–30	3–19	10–20 48–50	58–64 442–457	433–460	15–53		47–76 102–110	9–28
3	Climatic Controls and Climatic Elements	55–76	61–77	39–53	96–117	465–478	193–241	61–122	127–129	33–97
4	Climatic Types	99–180	81–368	103–446	120–142 239–399	478–488 10–20	243–284	123–192 421–423	131–138 380–682	100–140
5	The Origins of Surface Features	212–233		34–39	64–69 75–95	489–515	107–156	269–356	140–161	145–172
6	Major Types of Landforms	235–275	30–43	36–39	73–75	5–10 100–101 381–387	97–106 159–189	269–356	140–161	174–214
7	Natural Vegetation	182–210	50–55	53–54	162–187	527–529	311–334	193–238	203–224	
8	Soils	306–320	45–50	56–59	192–208	55–56 106–107 218, 346 285–289	289–309	239–267	167–182	216–229
9	Water Resources	374–398	55–59	59–60	144–153		59–63 72–96	357–376	184–201	253–275 377–380
10	Oceans and Seas	278–304	20–29		153–160		63–72	377–403	110–117	233–251
11	Fuel Minerals	354–365		84–86	215–225 414–418		499–516	181	225–233	354–377
12	Metallic Minerals	344–354		84–86	225–237		519–533		233–243	381–396
13	Physical Geography in Perspective			61–62	18–53 435–441	25–38 423–425	339–341 593–599		27–45 779–787	

xiii

QUICK REFERENCE TABLE TO STANDARD TEXTBOOKS

All figures refer to pages. See pages viii to xii for complete titles.

Chapter in this Outline	Topic	Murphey	Powers	Shaw	Strahler (Introd.)	Strahler	Trewartha et al. (Elements)	Trewartha et al. (Physical Elements)	Van Riper	White & Renner
1	The Field of Geography	1-9	1-3	3-17	1-2	1-2	v-vi	v-vi	1-3	3-10
2	The Planet Earth	21-26	229-236 535-543	19-39	3-40 422-435	5-90	1-42	1-42	11-42	600-621
3	Climatic Controls and Climatic Elements	69-77	237-329	56-74	42-100	109-177	45-127	45-127	155-244	33-47
4	Climatic Types	71-77	333-405	199-286	102-116 128-164	181-232	128-196	128-196	245-284	51-291
5	The Origins of Surface Features		7-87	93-98	230-401	259-496	202-257	202-257	43-90	343-354
6	Major Types of Landforms	134-146	88-138	100-115	224-230	260-261	258-360	258-360	91-154	355-414
7	Natural Vegetation	86-99	518-533	152-163	192-225		433-451	433-451	285-368	295-326
8	Soils	101-117	497-521	165-178	166-190	236-254	452-489	452-489	369-436	417-444
9	Water Resources	119-133	468-496	133-149	117-127 278-285		403-432	403-432	483-526	519-554
10	Oceans and Seas		139-149	117-131 76-78	242-245	93-104 138-147	361-395	361-395	527-568	555-576
11	Fuel Minerals	165, 547	417-430	180-194		454, 458, 474, 479	490-505	490-505	437-459	447-465 494-516
12	Metallic Minerals	165, 169	431-453	180-194			505-515	505-515	460-473	478-493
13	Physical Geography in Perspective	29-57 148-164 170-174	409-416	41-54					3-10	649-694

1

The Field of Geography

The term *geography* was coined by some ancient Greek scholar who combined two common words of his language, "ge" (the earth) and "graphein" (to write), to identify the science of the study of the earth. Since the literal meaning of the term does not indicate what is to be written about the earth, throughout its long history geography has meant different things to different people. This chapter presents a brief history of the development of geography, describes the modern concepts and methodology of the discipline, and discusses the place of physical geography in the field of geography as a whole.

THE HISTORICAL BACKGROUND OF GEOGRAPHY

The history of geographic study goes back to ancient scholars who speculated about the nature of the earth upon which they lived. Much of what ancient peoples believed about lands beyond their immediate surroundings was based upon legendary tales that had been passed down from generation to generation. The first important contributions to knowledge about the nature of the earth were made by learned men of the ancient Mediterranean world.

The Ancient Greek and Roman Geographers. During the five centuries that preceded the Christian Era, such Greek scholars as Herodotus, Aristotle, Eratosthenes, and Hipparchus were concerned with describing the habitable parts of the world and formulating theories regarding the true nature of the earth. They endeavored to apply the Greek principle of symmetry to the arrangement of unknown lands, conceiving these lands as corresponding to areas already explored. It was effectively proved that the earth was a sphere and its circumference was accurately computed. The concept that the world could be divided into temperate, torrid, and frigid zones based upon latitude, which was supported by Aristotle, became widely accepted and some attempts were made to solve the problem of depicting the curved surface of the earth on a flat sheet of paper. During this time the word "geography" became an accepted part of the Greek language. Some of the theories advanced by the Greeks had to be discarded, but centuries later many of their ideas were found to be correct.

Where the Greeks were concerned with theories of geography, the geographers of the Roman Empire were more interested in facts. They produced encyclopedic descriptions of the known world to help with the planning of military campaigns, the administration of provinces, and the development of trade. The most famous of these descriptive works were the seventeen volumes written by Strabo between 20 B.C. and A.D. 20 and the eight books written by Ptolemy around A.D. 140. The *Geography* by Ptolemy included the first atlas of maps ever compiled and generally summarized Greek knowledge about the earth. Although much of Ptolemy's work was later found to be inaccurate, it was preserved through the years, and a thousand years afterward in Western Europe his treatise was the chief source of information about the physical world.

Geography During the Middle Ages. Following the decline of the Roman Empire and during the Middle Ages geography received very little attention, for almost the only scholars were churchmen who devoted their energies to theological topics. Much of what had been learned about the earth in earlier times would have been lost entirely had not the Arabs preserved it during this period. The followers of Mohammed were interested in geography for they were a traveling and trading people, and in addition, certain tenets of their religion required that they have accurate information about direction, distance, and the location of places. Ptolemy's *Geography* was translated into Arabic, and Muslim geographers extended the horizons of the Greeks, preserved earlier knowledge, and formulated new concepts of their own. One important Arab contribution was the attempt to subdivide the latitudinal climatic zones of Aristotle into a larger number of zones separated by north-south as well as east-west lines.

Geography During the Renaissance. In the early part of the period of transition from medieval to modern times, interest in geography was revived by the Crusades and by the travels of Marco Polo and others. The growing desire for new trade routes to the Orient and the encouragement offered by such men as Prince Henry the Navigator of Portugal, who was keenly interested in exploration and geographical theory, led to the voyages of discovery during the fifteenth and sixteenth centuries. The western hemisphere was explored during these years and the general outlines of the great land masses of the earth became known. For several centuries the accepted task of the geographers was to record discoveries on maps and to write descriptions of the new lands.

Geography During the Eighteenth and Nineteenth Centuries. From the seventeenth century well into the nineteenth, European nations expanded their overseas territories and sent exploration and colonization parties to the Americas, Africa, and the Far East. Until the latter part of the eighteenth century, geographers were engaged in collecting data, compiling descriptions, and otherwise filling in the details of the world map; but by the 1800's, under the leadership of German scholars such as Kant, Humboldt, and Ritter, interest was shifted away from the gathering of facts toward the formulation of principles which would lead to the understanding of conditions which cause similarities and variations in landscapes to exist over the earth. Many of the leading geographers of this period had received their academic training in the natural sciences, particularly geology and botany, and geographic research tended to stress the dependence of man upon his physical environment. This "environmental determinism" still has a strong influence upon geographic thought.

MODERN GEOGRAPHY

The study of the earth and of man is so broad that there is still much diversity of opinion about what should or should not be included within the field of geography. There are so many definitions of the subject that someone has suggested, facetiously, that "geography is what the geographer studies."

Some Definitions of Geography. Many writers of geographic textbooks do not define their subject in specific terms, preferring to tell readers what the subject is about or the contributions it makes to their education. However, there are enough definitions in use today to illustrate the variety of views upon the subject of what is geography. Some of the more widely accepted definitions include:

Geography is the science of the earth's surface.

Geography is the study of the interrelationships between man and his environment.

Geography is the study of landscapes.

Geography is the science devoted to the study of the distribution of things on the earth.

Geography is the study of differences and similarities from place to place on the earth.

The Specialized Interests of Modern Geographers. In view of the numerous concepts regarding what should be contained within geography, and the broad scope of the subject, it is not surprising that professional geographers today tend to have specialized interests. Among the fields of specialization are human geography, historical geography, political geography, physical geography, urban geography, educational geography, cartography or the science of maps, land use, climatology, conservation, and geomorphology or the study of landforms. In addition, most professional geographers have a particular interest in some specific country or continental area, or in a climatic type such as the tropics, desert lands, or polar regions.

The Common Interests of Modern Geographers. Despite the diverse areas of specialization in the field of geography, there are basic factors which must be considered in any geographic study. No matter what his specific interest may be, a geographer will concern himself with the physical earth and with human beings. He will directly or indirectly relate his study to the answers to three questions:

1. Where are things located? This question involves the specific location of population groups, of economic activities, and of natural features, and the distribution patterns they form when plotted on maps. It also implies concern with the interrelationships between places.

2. How do people live in a particular area or place? The geographer examines the occupations of peoples in various parts

of the world, the products which are the result of these occupations, and settlement patterns.

3. Why do people live as they do in a particular area or place? This question involves both the study of the physical environment as a set of conditions which limit human activity in an area and an understanding of the people themselves. The *culture* of a people—their way of life that is an outgrowth of their desires, their abilities, and the knowledge that has been handed down by previous generations—determines the extent to which the natural environment will be utilized by them.

GEOGRAPHIC METHODS OF INVESTIGATION

Geography is both descriptive and explanatory. When it catalogs the characteristics of places it is descriptive; when it deals with the significance of these characteristics and their relationships to each other, it becomes an analytical science.

Approaches to Geographic Study. Geographic investigation is directed either toward some specific area or region or toward some particular element of the physical or cultural environment.

The systematic approach involves the study of one or more aspects of the landscape separately. Topics such as landforms, climate, vegetation, soils, mineral resources, population, land use, and industries are examined in terms of their various components and their distribution.

The regional approach involves the examination of selected areas or regions that have one or more characteristics in common. Regions are studied in terms of their total aspects, both physical and human, with the objective of understanding individual regions and the similarities and differences that exist between regions in various parts of the earth.

Geographic Methods. Geography makes use of the established methods of scientific inquiry. It employs both deductive and inductive reasoning to formulate explanations for features observed on the earth. The use of induction (from the particular to the general) makes it possible to develop principles from observed phenomena; and by deduction (from the general to the specific), principles can be applied to observed phenomena.

The initial step in geographic investigation (as in any other science) is careful observation and the quantitative measurement of the natural or cultural phenomena being studied. Like other scientists the geographer may keep a verbal or statistical record of his observations, but he also enters these observations upon detailed maps. From these records, geographic features can be classified and observed patterns and apparent relationships are noted. After this analysis, an attempt is made to formulate *hypotheses* or tentative explanations for the phenomena. The geographer often finds it difficult to test his hypotheses by experimentation, but he endeavors to validate them by applying them in several different parts of the world. If the applications confirm the predictions of an hypothesis, the hypothesis may be referred to as a *theory,* or stated explanation of causes and relationships. When a theory becomes generally accepted by other scholars in the field of geography, it acquires the status of a *geographic principle.*

GEOGRAPHY AMONG THE SCIENCES

Because it deals with both natural and human phenomena geography occupies a middle ground between the physical and social sciences. The types of geography which emphasize surface features of the earth, climate, vegetation, animal life, soils, and mineral resources belong within the realm of the natural sciences and form the various subdivisions of physical geography. Those which deal with population, culture groups, political units, economic activities, and settlement patterns are part of the social sciences and form the branches of human or cultural geography.

Although geography utilizes the materials of many other disciplines, the subject of geography is much more than the mere collection and compilation of the various data that have been assembled separately by the geologist, the meteorologist, the botanist, the sociologist, the economist, or the anthropologist. The function of geography is to study the combination of features which make up the various regions of the earth, to investigate the relationships between the physical and cultural characteristics of areas, and to explain the reasons for differences and similarities which exist between areas of the earth.

PHYSICAL GEOGRAPHY

The basic objective of physical geography, the subject of this book, is to provide an understanding of the elements of the natural environment and an appreciation of the earth as the home of man. Although its major theme involves description and interpretation of physical features of the earth, physical geography is also concerned with the significance of areal differences and with the factors which have caused the existing structural patterns.

In a systematic approach which we shall follow in this volume, the several elements of the physical environment—climatic conditions, surface features, natural vegetation, soils, water resources, and mineral resources—will be discussed separately. First, the factors which cause an environmental element to differ from place to place are examined; each element is classified into types, and a description of the nature and distribution of these types over the surface of the earth is given. The description of world patterns will show how the several elements such as climate, natural vegetation, and soils are related to each other, and will demonstrate the limitations that environment imposes upon human activity in various parts of the world.

SUPPLEMENTARY READING

Baker, J. N. L. *History of Geography.* New York: Barnes & Noble, Inc., 1963.

Broek, Jan O. M. *Geography: Its Scope and Spirit.* Columbus: Charles E. Merrill Books, Inc., 1965.

Freeman, T. W. *A Hundred Years of Geography.* Chicago: Aldine Publishing Co., 1961.

Hartshorne, Richard. *The Nature of Geography.* Washington, D.C.: Association of American Geographers, 1949.

———. *Perspective on the Nature of Geography.* Chicago: Rand McNally & Co., 1959.

James, Preston E. (ed.). *New Viewpoints in Geography.* 29th Yearbook of the National Council for the Social Studies. Washington, D.C., 1959.

James, Preston E., and Jones, Clarence F. (eds.). *American Geography: Inventory and Prospect.* Syracuse: Syracuse University Press, 1954.

Sauer, Carl O. *Land and Life: A Selection of the Writings of Carl O. Sauer.* ed. by John Leighly. Berkeley: University of California Press, 1963.

2

The Planet Earth

Many of the geographic conditions which are familiar to people all over the world have their origins in the shape, size, and movements of the earth. The major elements of the natural environment derive many of their basic characteristics from the nature of the earth itself and from the earth's relationship to the sun. Human life everywhere is influenced by environmental factors and thus by the nature of the planet.

SIZE AND SHAPE OF THE EARTH

The earth is one of the nine planets of the solar system which revolve about the sun. (See Fig. 1.) Although it has high mountains and great ocean depths, and is slightly flattened at the poles, the earth may be regarded for all practical purposes as if it were a sphere. (It is an oblate spheroid.) Variation from exact sphericity is less than one per cent of its 4,000-mile radius and if the earth were accurately reduced to the comparative size of an orange it would appear as a very smooth ball. The earth, with a diameter of nearly 8,000 miles and a circumference of approximately 25,000 miles, is fifth among the planets in size; its diameter is less than one-tenth that of Jupiter, the largest planet, and two and one-half times that of Mercury, the smallest. The area of the earth's surface is approximately 197 million square miles, with a total volume of about 250 billion cubic miles.

EARTH-SUN RELATIONSHIPS

The earth, like its sister planets, revolves around the sun. Its movements, accompanied by certain other relationships, cause day and night, the seasons, and basic differences in climate.

8

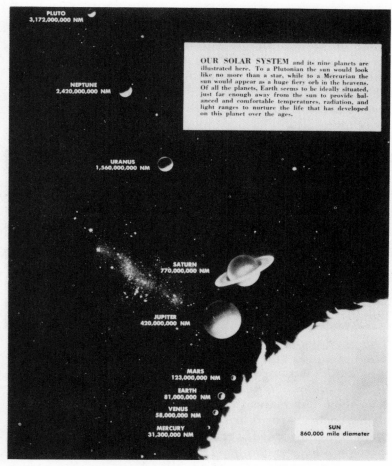

OUR SOLAR SYSTEM and its nine planets are illustrated here. To a Plutonian the sun would look like no more than a star, while to a Mercurian the sun would appear as a huge fiery orb in the heavens. Of all the planets, Earth seems to be ideally situated, just far enough away from the sun to provide balanced and comfortable temperatures, radiation, and light ranges to nurture the life that has developed on this planet over the ages.

PLUTO
3,172,000,000 NM

NEPTUNE
2,420,000,000 NM

URANUS
1,560,000,000 NM

SATURN
770,000,000 NM

JUPITER
420,000,000 NM

MARS
123,000,000 NM

EARTH
81,000,000 NM

VENUS
58,000,000 NM

MERCURY
31,300,000 NM

SUN
860,000 mile diameter

Fig. 1. The solar system. NM is an abbreviation for nautical miles. (Courtesy of United States Air Force, from AFM 105-5, Weather for Aircrews.)

Revolution. The earth is held in its place within the solar system by gravitational attraction emanating from the other planets as they all revolve around the sun. The pull of gravity is nearly uniform, but not completely so, because the distance between the earth and the sun, which averages some 93,000,000 miles, varies from 91,500,000 miles in January to 94,500,000 in

July. The earth completes one revolution around the sun in each solar year at the average speed of about 18.5 miles per second. (Since the earth rotates on its axis 365¼ times while completing one revolution around the sun, the solar year has 365¼ days.) The path that the earth follows as it moves around the sun is called its *orbit*. An imaginary level plane passing through the sun and connecting all points on the earth's orbit is referred to as the *plane of the ecliptic*.

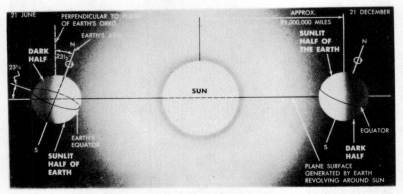

Fig. 2. Two positions of the earth in its orbit. Note axial inclination and parallelism. (COURTESY OF UNITED STATES AIR FORCE, FROM AFM 105-5, WEATHER FOR AIRCREWS.)

Rotation. As the earth journeys about the sun it turns, or rotates, on an imaginary axis the ends of which are the North and South Poles. The speed of rotation of the earth ranges from zero at the poles to approximately 1,037 miles per hour at the equator, midway between the poles. The earth makes a complete rotation on its axis once every twenty-four hours, the half of the earth that is exposed to the sun being in daylight and the other half in darkness. Rotation, then, causes the phenomena of day and night and fixes the length of days. Since the earth rotates from west to east the sun appears to rise in the east and set in the west, and daylight on a continent always occurs first in its most easterly portions. Rotation also creates a centrifugal force which causes the earth to have a slight bulge at the equator, and it has a deflective effect upon the movement of winds and ocean currents.

Axial Inclination and Parallelism. The axis upon which the earth rotates is always inclined 23½ degrees away from perpendicular to the plane of the ecliptic and its position at any one time of the year is parallel to that at any other time of the year. (See Fig. 2.) These two characteristics of axial inclination and parallelism, combined with revolution and rotation, cause the amount of light received from the sun to vary from one part of the earth to another, and from one time of the year to another at a particular location. Because of inclination of the earth's axis, one half of the earth is always tilted toward the sun and the other half away from it. Parallelism of the axis causes the northern half of the earth (the northern hemisphere) to be tilted toward the sun for part of the year and away from it during another part; in the southern hemisphere the seasons of inclination toward or away from the sun are reversed. Thus during the month of June the northern hemisphere is tilted toward the sun and, as the earth rotates on its axis, experiences sunlight for more than half of the twenty-four hour period. (See Figs. 2 and 3.) At the same time the southern hemisphere is inclined away from the sun and has daylight for less

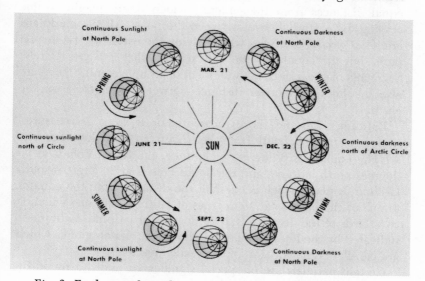

Fig. 3. Earth-sun relationships. Note sunlight at different seasons in the northern hemisphere. (COURTESY OF UNITED STATES AIR FORCE, FROM AFM 105-5, WEATHER FOR AIRCREWS.)

than half of the twenty-four hour period involved in one rotation. The opposite occurs in January, when the southern hemisphere is inclined toward the sun. In March and September the earth's axis is in such a position that sunlight is equally distributed between the northern and southern halves of the earth.

LOCATION OF PLACES ON THE EARTH

On a sphere, such as the earth, there are no corners, no sides, no beginning or end, and only two fixed points (the North and South Poles, fixed by earth rotation) from which the exact location of places can be determined. The system which has been devised for establishing the precise location of places is based upon the shape and external relations of the earth. It consists of a system of coordinates, or north-south and east-west lines, measured off in degrees. Since the earth is for most practical purposes a sphere, these reference lines consist of two sets of circles, each circle containing 360 degrees. The north-south circles, known as *meridians,* pass through the North and South Poles. The east-west segments of the earth grid, called *parallels,* circle the earth at equal distances from the *equator,* which is an imaginary line circling the earth half way between the poles. All the meridians are *great circles,* or circles which divide the earth into two equal parts, but the equator is the only parallel that is a great circle. Segments of great circles, those mentioned above and others, are also the lines of shortest distance between two places on the earth.

Latitude. Distance north or south, or *latitude,* is measured in degrees north or south from the equator to the poles. (See Fig. 4.) The equator is 0 degrees of latitude, the North Pole is at 90 degrees north latitude, and the South Pole is at 90 degrees south latitude. A place which is one-half the distance from the equator to one of the poles is at 45 degrees of latitude, and one which is two-thirds of the distance is at 60 degrees of latitude. Latitude is indicated by the lines on maps and by the circles on globes which are parallel to the equator and are called parallels.

Certain parallels are of special significance and are found on most maps:

The equator, or 0 degrees of latitude, is the base line for latitude measurements and divides the earth into northern and

Fig. 4. Earth coordinates. The map projection is oblique orthographic. The letters NP indicate the location of the North Pole.

southern hemispheres. Along the equator days and nights are of almost equal length throughout the year. The sun appears directly overhead on the equator at noon about March 21 [1] and September 22 each year.

The *Tropic of Cancer* and the *Tropic of Capricorn* are the parallels of 23½ degrees north and south, respectively. Along them the sun is directly overhead at noon for only one day of the year, about June 21 in the northern hemisphere and about December 22 in the southern hemisphere. The combined effects of earth

---

[1] These are the times of the vernal equinox and the autumnal equinox, respectively. The equinoxes do not occur on precisely the same date each year because of the man-made custom of using the "leap year" to adjust the calendar to the solar year.

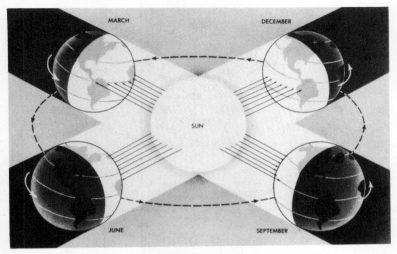

Fig. 5. Seasonal migration of the direct rays of the sun. (COURTESY OF UNITED STATES AIR FORCE, FROM AFM 105-5, WEATHER FOR AIR-CREWS.)

rotation, revolution, inclination, and parallelism cause the rays of the sun to be directly overhead at different locations throughout the twelve-month period (see Fig. 5), but poleward of the Tropics of Cancer and Capricorn the sun is never directly overhead. The part of the earth lying between the parallels of 23½ degrees north and 23½ degrees south is generally thought of as the "low latitudes" or the "tropics."

The *Arctic Circle* and the *Antarctic Circle* are the parallels of 66½ degrees north and south, respectively. They mark the place in either hemisphere where there is one day with twenty-four hours of daylight and one with twenty-four hours of darkness in each year. Poleward of these circles the length of the longest night (or day) increases until, theoretically, it is six months long at the poles. In both hemispheres the areas between the tropics and the circles are commonly thought of as the "midlatitudes," and the areas poleward from the two circles are known as the "high latitudes" or "polar areas."

Longitude.   Position east and west, or *longitude,* is computed from a line which extends from the North Pole to the South Pole and passes through an astronomical observatory located in Greenwich, England, a suburb of London. This starting line, known as the *prime meridian* or *Greenwich meridian*, is at 0 degrees of longitude, and longitude is measured up to 180 degrees east or west of this line. A place one-quarter of the way around the world from Greenwich in a westerly direction would have longitude of 90 degrees west, and one the same distance in the other direction would be located at 90 degrees east. Places halfway around the world from Greenwich are at 180 degrees of longitude (no east or west should be indicated). Longitude is marked on maps and globes by the lines and circles called meridians.

The *international date line* is the meridian of 180 degrees throughout most of its length and is the line where east-west navigators correct their calendars. Here days begin and end, and when this line is crossed, the date and day of the week must change. Passengers of aircraft flying westward advance their calendars one day upon crossing the date line; for example, they pass from Tuesday to Thursday and omit Wednesday. Going eastward across the date line, travelers set their calendars back one day; thus they repeat a day as, for example, having two Tuesdays with the same date of the month. In ship travel the adjustment of the calendar is made at midnight after the date line is crossed.

Place Location. Any point on the surface of the earth can be accurately located by latitude and longitude. One degree of latitude equals 69 miles (circumference of the earth divided by the number of degrees, $25,000 \div 360 = 69.4$), and the length of a degree of longitude varies from 69 miles at the equator to zero at the poles. For more exact location of specific places, degrees of latitude and longitude are subdivided into 60 minutes and each minute into 60 seconds. The position of any place is found at the intersection of the parallel which determines its latitude with the meridian which determines its longitude. Thus, to find the location of Tecumseh, Michigan (42°N., 84°W.) on a map, one would only need to follow along the 42°N. parallel until it intersected with the 84°W. meridian; but to locate Ann Arbor, Michigan (42°17′N., 83°44′W.), one would need to interpolate between the meridians and parallels that were shown on the map being used.

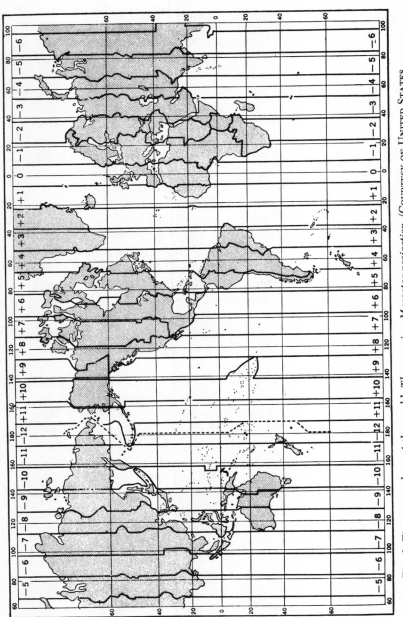

Fig. 6. Time zone chart of the world. The map is a Mercator projection. (COURTESY OF UNITED STATES NAVY DEPARTMENT, FROM UNITED STATES HYDROGRAPHIC OFFICE PUBLICATION No. 9.)

Longitude and Time. In addition to its usefulness in locating places, longitude serves as the basis for determining time. Since the earth makes a complete rotation on its axis once every twenty-four hours, and there are 360 degrees of longitude, the earth rotates at a speed of 15 degrees each hour. Years ago, each community computed its time according to that of the nearest meridian, or "sun time," but the practice became awkward as transportation and communication became faster. Now most places follow the time of standard time belts which are zones that have been established on either side of the meridians that are divisible by 15 (see Fig. 6). These zones do not follow straight north-south lines but are often quite irregular according to local convenience. Because the earth rotates toward the east, the hour at easterly places is always ahead of the time at places to the west. Thus, when it is 12:00 noon on a particular day at London (0° longitude), it is 2:00 P.M. at Leningrad (30°20′E. longitude), 9:00 A.M. at Rio de Janeiro (43°20′W. longitude), and 6:00 A.M. at Chicago (87°40′W. longitude).

MAPS

The features which make up the surface of the earth are too large to be comprehended by direct sight. The outlines of a continent or the locational relationships between countries are much beyond the range of human vision. To reduce these features to comprehensible size so that they may be observed and studied, geographers devised maps, which are graphic representations of all or part of the earth's surface. Maps are the most valuable tool of geography. They are constructed by the processes of locating and measuring things on the surface of the earth and then recording these data by reductions on flat planes or spherical globes. Only a globe can show earth features correctly, but globes are unwieldy in size and shape. Maps on flat planes are used almost universally because they are convenient to carry, can be reproduced easily, and can be drawn to almost any scale.

To derive utmost benefit from maps, the student must be familiar with map scales, map projections, and map symbols.

Map Scales. A map scale is the ratio between linear distance on a map and the true measurement of the same distance on the earth. For example, if a certain city lot on a map measures one inch by one inch and on the ground the lot measures 100 feet by 100 feet, the scale of the map is one inch equal to 100 feet. This ratio, or scale, is always expressed by giving the map measurement first and the actual measurement last. There are three ways of expressing map scale:

1. Verbal or representative scale, in which the ratio is represented by two units presumably known to the map reader. A common scale of this type is "one inch to one mile." Such scales are easy to measure with the eye but have the defect that they are understandable only to those who are familiar with the units used. "One inch to one mile" would mean little to a Frenchman while "one centimeter to one kilometer" would have no meaning for most Americans.

2. Numerical or fractional scale, which does not specify any units but gives two numbers, the first of which represents the map and the second the earth. A scale such as 1:50,000 indicates that one of any unit (inch, centimeter, foot, or meter) may be used and designates the ratio between distance on the map and distance in the same area on the earth. A scale of this type may also be written in the form $1/50,000$ or $\dfrac{1}{50,000}$.

3. Graphic scale, which divides a line into units, making it possible to measure distances on the map by comparing them with the units. Scales of this type are usually helpful for eye measurements of distance but can also be used for accurate work if made on an exact basis. The graphic scale for a map constructed on the scale of "one inch equals five miles" would consist of a line several inches long having each inch from zero labeled in multiples of five. It would usually have one segment subdivided into five parts to indicate the length of one mile.

Often there is confusion in the use of the terms "large scale maps" and "small scale maps." A large scale map is one in which a relatively large sheet of paper is used to represent a small part of the earth's surface. A small scale map is the opposite; if the entire world is shown on a map of book page size or even on a large wall map, the scale is very small. A good way to remember this is to think in terms of fractions; a 1:50,000 map is a much larger scale than a 1:2,000,000 map because a fraction of one fiftythousandth is a much larger fraction than one two-millionth.

Map Projections. Because the curved surface of the earth cannot be fitted on a flat plane without distortion, globes are the only true maps. Since globes, in comparison with flat maps, are rather inconvenient to use, various systems have been devised for representing earth areas on flat sheets of paper. These are called map projections. A *map projection* is defined as any orderly arrangement of meridians and parallels upon which a map can be drawn. All map projections show some distortion and the larger the area depicted on a map the greater the distortion. Each projection is designed to control some type of distortion which results from attempting to represent the round earth on a flat sheet of paper, and to secure some desired quality or property.

The properties of map projections are

1. *Equal-area* or equivalence, in which areas on a map are shown in true relationship to the areas they occupy on the earth. Any one area has the same size relationship to any other area that would be found on a globe. Projections with this quality may also have the property of equal-distance but they often distort shapes and direction.

2. *True-shape* or conformality, in which the shapes of land and water bodies are accurately represented. In order to secure this quality, the scale must be varied from one part of the map to another and areas will be distorted in size away from the center.

3. *True-direction* or azimuthal, in which direction from the center of the map is truly represented. Some types of projections show true direction on all portions of the map.

CLASSIFICATION OF MAP PROJECTIONS. Map projections may be classified according to the manner in which the grids are constructed. All have certain advantages and disadvantages.

1. *Rectangular projections* such as Mercator, cylindrical equal spaced, and cylindrical equal-area (see Fig. 7), have both parallels and meridians represented by parallel lines to form a network of rectangles. The several types differ from each other in the spacing of the parallels.

Distortion is largely longitudinal, particularly in the high latitudes.

Advantages of these projections are that both parallels and meridians are straight lines, making it easy to compare places having the same latitude or longitude. Compass directions are

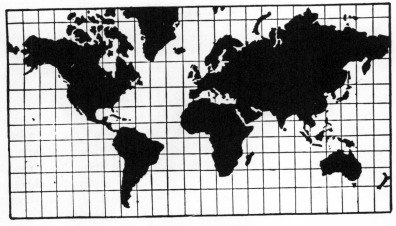

MERCATOR PROJECTION.

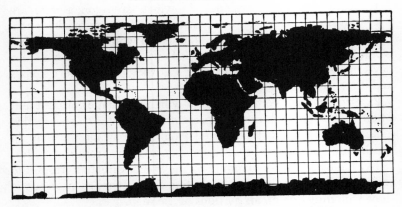

CYLINDRICAL EQUAL SPACED PROJECTION.

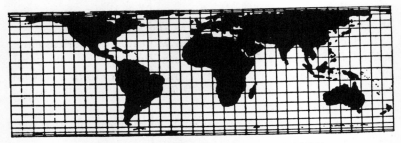

CYLINDRICAL EQUAL-AREA PROJECTION.

Fig. 7. *Rectangular projections.* (FROM UNITED STATES COAST AND GEODETIC SURVEY PUBLICATIONS.)

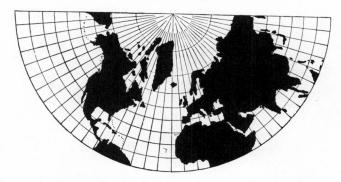

Fig. 8. *Conic projection of the northern hemisphere. Tangency is at 30 degrees north.* (AFTER UNITED STATES COAST AND GEODETIC SURVEY.)

true along grid lines and with the Mercator projection are true everywhere. The principal use of rectangular projections is for navigational purposes.

Disadvantages result from distortion in the size of areas and the variation from true scale away from the equator. Rectangular projections misrepresent the size and shape of land areas in the polar regions.

2. *Conic projections,* such as the true conic (see Fig. 8) and modified conic (Bonne, Fig. 9, page 22, and polyconic, Fig. 19, page 41) types, have been developed from the idea of a cone fitted to a globe tangent along some parallel. Parallels appear as arcs of circles, with meridians being either radiating straight lines or corresponding curves.

Distortion increases in either direction from the tangent line or standard parallel. This distortion is so great with increasing distances that the conics are useful for representing only one hemisphere or continent.

Advantages result from the fact that most of these projections are easily constructed and that they are good for portraying single countries or areas smaller than hemispheres. By adjustment of the position of the parallels, the projections can be made either equal-area or conformal but not both on the same map.

Disadvantages result from the limitation on the size of areas that can be depicted; these projections are unsatisfactory for showing the entire earth. They lack constant direction.

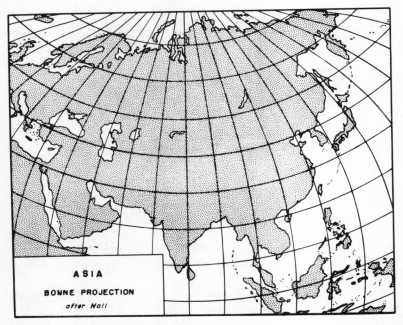

Fig. 9. Bonne projection of Asia. (AFTER MAP BY ROBERT B. HALL.)

3. *Elliptical projections* such as the Mollweide, sinusoidal, and Aitoff (see Fig. 10) have a grid whereby the entire earth is represented as an oval. Parallels are usually (but not always) horizontal and the meridians are curved lines. Distance from pole to pole is usually half the length of the equator.

Distortion is great near the margins of the map, particularly in the high latitudes, but not so great as with the rectangular projections.

Advantages lie in the approximation of equal area, for some are truly equal-area, and in the delineation of equal latitudes by horizontal lines. Maps of this type are best for representing the entire world.

Disadvantages result from the absence of true north-south direction and from the general compression of shapes in the high latitudes.

4. *Interrupted projections,* such as Goode's homolosine, Finch's interruption of Aitoff's projection, and the interrupted Mollweide,

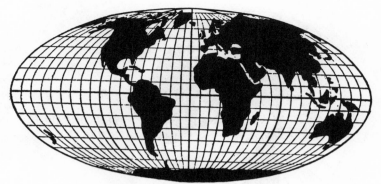

MOLLWEIDE PROJECTION.

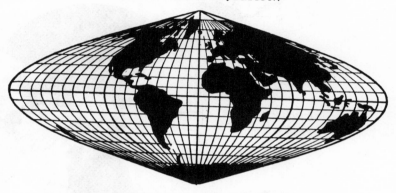

SINUSOIDAL PROJECTION.

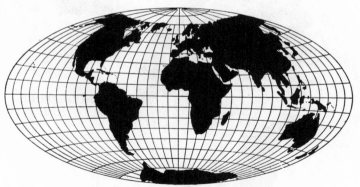

AITOFF PROJECTION.

Fig. 10. Elliptical projections. (FROM UNITED STATES COAST AND GEODETIC SURVEY PUBLICATIONS.)

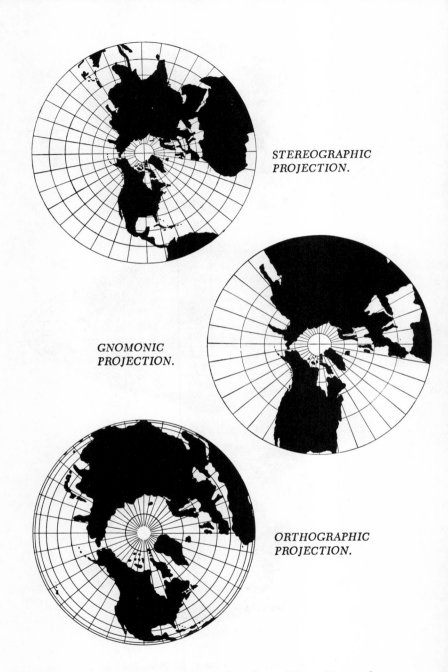

STEREOGRAPHIC
PROJECTION.

GNOMONIC
PROJECTION.

ORTHOGRAPHIC
PROJECTION.

Fig. 11. Azimuthal projections, polar phase. (FROM UNITED STATES
COAST AND GEODETIC SURVEY PUBLICATIONS.)

show the oceans split and the continents shifted close together. These projections, which are shown in many atlases and textbooks, are variations of the elliptical group described above. Interrupting attempts to reduce errors of shape, to retain the true size of land areas, and to secure the greatest possible land surface on a small scale map. To produce his homolosine projection, J. Paul Goode used the sinusoidal projection from the equator to 40°, Mollweide's projection from 40° to the poles, and split the oceans. V. C. Finch interrupted the Aitoff projection by eliminating some of the landless areas and by moving Australia and New Zealand over into the position occupied by the Indian Ocean. The author of this volume handled the Philip drawing of Mollweide's projection in a similar fashion to obtain a map that would be useful for portraying world patterns of environmental phenomena (see Figs. 23, 37, and 38, pages 56, 126, and 140). Other projections of this type have been constructed with the continents interrupted and entire ocean basins emphasized.

5. *Azimuthal projections* such as the orthographic, stereographic, and gnomonic (see Fig. 11) are sometimes known as "global maps for the air age." They are developed by projecting meridians and parallels from a globe onto a plane surface. Most have equatorial, polar, and oblique phases (Fig. 4, page 13, illustrates oblique orthographic) and they differ from each other in the point from which the projection starts. Only the polar aspect is illustrated here. These projections tend to be radial in nature and appear as circles.

Distortion increases away from a central point and these projections cannot be used to show the entire earth on a single map.

Advantages of the azimuthal projections are that they can show hemispheres in their natural groupings. Since they appear as circles they emphasize to students the spherical shape of the earth. They have specialized uses such as for portraying great circle distances, air routes, polar lands, and communication radio lines. These projections are often employed as illustrations in popular literature.

Disadvantages result from their highly specialized uses, their unsuitability for showing the entire earth, and their lack of equivalence and/or conformality near their margins.

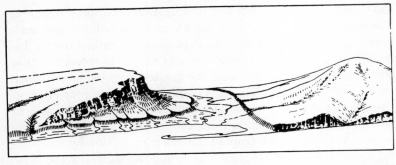

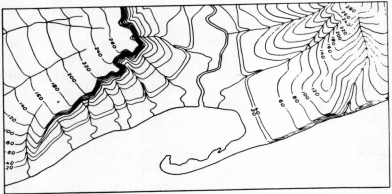

Fig. 12. Hachures and contour lines. Two ways of showing the surface configuration of the same area. (FROM UNITED STATES GEOLOGICAL SURVEY.)

Map Symbols. Symbols on a map represent phenomena that actually appear on the surface of the earth. To understand a map it is necessary to reverse the process and visualize the nature of the area portrayed from the symbols being utilized. Some symbols designate areas large enough to be shown to scale. These areas may be bounded by lines and identified by colors or markings which are explained in a key or legend on the map. Other symbols are in the nature of points or lines which represent boundaries and locations which have no area, or an area which is too small to be shown at scale. Maps employ symbols in many combinations. In terms of their symbols maps can be classified into four types:

1. Maps which show areal extent, form, or outline. These utilize

area and line symbols and often have colors, or black and white shadings, to accentuate the areas being shown. Maps depicting the political areas of nations or the states of countries are examples of this type.

2. Maps which show patterns of arrangement. These illustrate road, street, or drainage patterns. They employ principally point and line symbols.

3. Maps which show surface configuration. Several devices are utilized on maps to indicate the nature of the land surface.

Contour lines, or lines which connect points having the same elevation, are very common devices that are used to represent surface configuration (see Fig. 12). On maps of this type, usually called topographic maps, lines representing the same elevation are drawn at arbitrarily selected intervals. Areas with steep slopes will have the lines close together while level areas, or gently sloping areas, will have the lines widely spaced.

Hachures are short lines drawn parallel to the slope of the land. In one system, the steeper the slope the heavier the line is drawn; in another, the lines are all the same width but are placed closer together where the slopes are steep (see Fig. 12). Maps showing detailed relief of small areas by this device are called block diagrams.

Plastic shading produces a model-like effect by the distribution of light and shadow (see Fig. 13). Steep slopes are in shadow and have dark shading; the more gentle the slope the lighter the shading. Modern topographic maps frequently use a combination of plastic shading and contour lines.

4. Maps which show areal distribution of phenomena. Many devices are used to show the areal distribution of actual or relative quantity of various phenomena. Maps using the most common of these devices are:

a) Isarithmic and isopleth maps, which employ the principle of the contour line. Isarithms are lines on a map which connect points having an equal measure of some individual quantity. The lines represent actual measurements: among the different kinds of isarithms, in addition to contour lines, are *isotherms* which connect points having equal temperatures (see Fig. 16, page 34); *isobars* which connect places having the same barometric pressure; and *isohyets* which connect places having the same amount of pre-

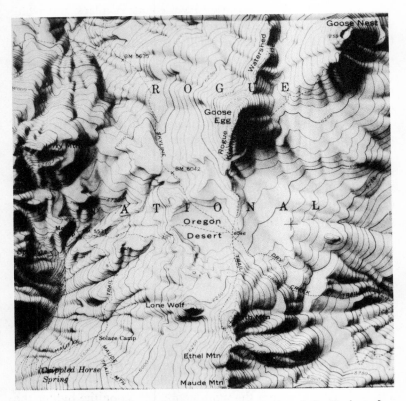

Fig. 13. *Plastic shading and contour lines. A section of the Geological Survey's Crater Lake National Park and Vicinity topographic map, with shaded relief overprint.*

cipitation. Lines which represent ratios, or relative values, are called *isopleths.*

b) *Dot maps,* which are generally used to show relative density of some particular quantity—population, crop land, a crop, animals, or structures. A basic value is selected for one dot and the number placed in any area is determined by the nearest whole unit of the dot value. Maps of this type produce shades of light and dark, depending upon the number of dots per unit of area. Dot maps are designed to give general impressions only, as readers are not expected to count the dots.

c) *Cartograms*, which are not actually maps but are map backgrounds with various types of symbols placed upon them to show distribution and comparative values. They utilize variously sized cubes, circles, spheres, figures, and shapes to give visual impressions of varying quantities.

SUPPLEMENTARY READING

Chamberlin, Wellman. *The Round Earth on Flat Paper*. Washington, D.C.: National Geographic Society, 1947.

Deetz, Charles H., and Adams, Oscar S. *Elements of Map Projection*. U.S. Department of Commerce, Special Publication No. 68. Washington, D.C.: Government Printing Office, 1945.

Greenhood, David. *Mapping*. Rev. ed. Chicago: University of Chicago Press, 1963.

Harrison, Lucia C. *Sun, Earth, Time, and Man*. Chicago: Rand McNally & Co., 1960.

Raisz, Erwin J. *Principles of Cartography*. New York: McGraw-Hill Book Co., Inc., 1962.

Robinson, Arthur H. *Elements of Cartography*. 2nd ed. New York: John Wiley & Sons, Inc., 1960.

Spurr, Stephen H. *Photogrammetry and Photo-interpretation*. 2nd ed. New York: Ronald Press, Inc., 1960.

3

Climatic Controls and Climatic Elements

Climate is one of the most important features of the natural environment which affect man. In one way or another climate influences all aspects of human life: the production of food, man's clothing and the kind of home he builds, economic activities, and even human energy. In addition to its direct effects upon man, climate exerts considerable influence upon other elements of the natural environment. The natural vegetation of an area reflects its climate, soil types are greatly affected by rainfall and temperature, and landforms vary in accordance with types of weathering and erosion found under different climatic conditions.

The study of climate is concerned with the earth's atmospheric conditions. Climate is a statistical concept—the record of weather history. *Weather* may be defined as the condition of the atmosphere at a place at a particular time, and *climate* is a generalized characterization of the diversified weather conditions of a place over a long period of time. The weather of a place at a given moment is a combination of the climatic elements of temperature, moisture, atmospheric pressure, and wind. Each climatic element results from certain phenomena called climatic controls and each is distributed over the surface of the earth in a pattern different from the other elements. Thus climatic controls acting upon climatic elements cause climatic differences over the face of the earth. Although each place on the earth has its own climate, areas which have the same general characteristics may be grouped together to form climatic types.

CLIMATIC CONTROLS

The climatic controls, acting together, determine the weather and climate of all places on the earth. They cause some places to be hot and some to be cold, some to be rainy and others dry, some to have the same weather throughout the year and others to have great seasonal variations in climate. An understanding of climatic controls helps us to understand many of the basic causes for similarities and differences between regions of the earth.

The climatic controls are latitude, land and water distribution, pressure and winds, air masses and storms, ocean currents, altitude, and mountain barriers.

Latitude. Latitude has great influence upon the climatic element of temperature because the latitude of a place—that is, its distance north or south of the equator—largely determines the amount of heat or energy, called *insolation,* which that place receives from the sun. Through its influence upon temperature, latitude also indirectly affects the direction of air movement.

LATITUDE AND TEMPERATURE. Since the sun is the source of most of the heat on the earth, the amount of insolation received at any place has a major effect upon the temperature at that location. The amount of heat received depends upon two factors:

1. The angle at which the sun's rays strike the earth. (See Fig. 14.) A place receives more heat when the sun is directly overhead than when the sun is low in the sky because the more vertical rays are concentrated on a relatively small area of the earth and the rays pass through a thinner portion of the earth's atmosphere.

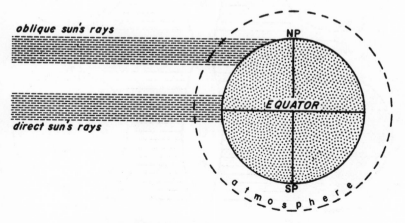

Fig. 14. Angle of the sun's rays and insolation.

The atmosphere contains water vapor, dust particles, and other impurities, all of which tend to disperse heat before it reaches the earth; thus, the less atmosphere the rays must penetrate, the less heat is lost.

Because of earth rotation, earth revolution, axial inclination, and axial parallelism, the sun can be directly overhead or perpendicular at local noon only in that portion of the earth lying between the Tropics of Capricorn and Cancer. (See Fig. 15.) Poleward of the two Tropics, the sun's rays are oblique to the surface of the earth throughout the year, and the angle of obliqueness becomes smaller during the winter season. At the North and South Poles the sun is never more than 23½ degrees above the horizon, and during winter at the poles the sun does not appear above the horizon at all.

2. The number of hours of daylight. As it revolves around the sun, the earth makes one complete rotation on its axis every twenty-four hours; the half of the earth facing the sun is in day-

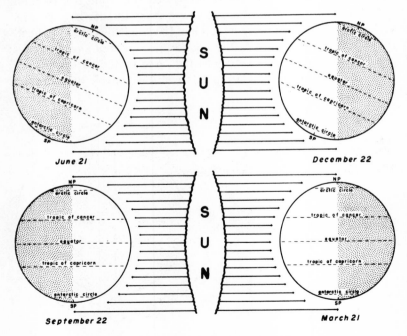

Fig. 15. *Seasonal variations in insolation.*

light and the half away from it is in darkness (Fig. 2, page 10). Because of inclination of the earth's axis and its parallelism, the northern hemisphere is tilted toward the sun and has longer days and warmer temperatures from March to September, while the southern hemisphere has shorter days and cooler temperatures. From September to March, the southern hemisphere enjoys longer days and greater insolation. (See Fig. 3, page 11.)

LATITUDE AND WINDS. The uneven distribution of heat is one of the causes of air movement on the earth. Air that is cool tends to be heavy and settling while air that is warm tends to be light and buoyant. The heavier air from higher latitudes often flows away from these areas of cold and moves toward areas of heat in the warmer latitudes near the equator. The contribution of latitudinal differences to the circulation of the atmosphere will be discussed more fully under the heading "Pressure and Winds."

Land and Water Distribution. Since land and water heat and cool at different rates, the arrangement of large land masses and wide expanses of ocean water on the earth greatly affects the distribution of temperature and influences the direction of air movement.

INFLUENCE UPON TEMPERATURE. Land surfaces heat and cool more rapidly than water surfaces because:

1. The specific heat of water is higher than that of land. Two to five times as much heat is required to raise the temperature of water one degree as for an equal volume of dry earth.

2. Water is mobile, and the mixing of surface and deep water disperses the heat from the sun throughout the volume of water.

3. Water is more transparent than land; the warming rays of the sun penetrate water more deeply and diffuse their heat. Land is opaque and the heat it receives is retained at the surface.

INFLUENCE UPON AIR MOVEMENT. Since land surfaces react to temperature changes more quickly than does water, large land masses tend to be areas of cold and settling air in winter and areas of warm and rising air in summer. The reverse is true over the oceans and seas, where air is cooler in summer and warmer in winter than the air over land masses, particularly in the middle latitudes where seasonal temperature changes are greatest. Thus air movement tends to be from the great oceans toward large land masses during the summer season and from the continents toward seas in the winter time.

CONTINENTAL AND MARITIME CLIMATES. There are considerable climatic differences between areas in the interiors of large

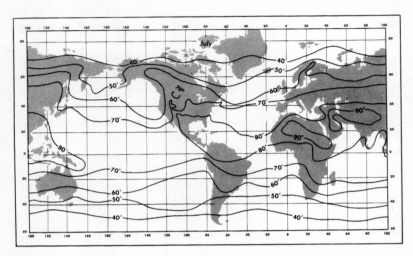

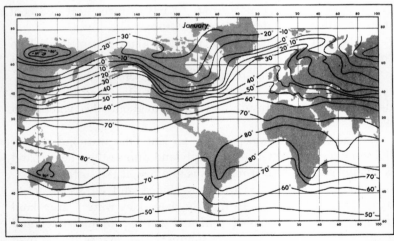

Fig. 16. Distribution of mean temperatures. Isotherms are in degrees Fahrenheit. The maps are drawn on a Mercator projection. (COURTESY OF UNITED STATES AIR FORCE, FROM AFM 105-5, WEATHER FOR AIRCREWS.)

land masses and those regions near the sea. Areas in the far interior of continents, particularly in the middle latitudes, have warm-to-hot summers and cool-to-cold winters and are said to have *continental climate*. They are subject to great seasonal variation in temperature.

Areas located along the coasts of the great oceans, particularly where winds blow from the sea to the land much of the year, have relatively little difference between summer and winter temperatures and are said to have *maritime climate*. They are characterized by small seasonal temperature changes.

A graphic illustration of the seasonal temperature changes which occur in interior land regions is shown in Figure 16, where the isotherms turn sharply poleward over the land masses in the northern hemisphere during July, and bend equatorward in January.

Pressure and Winds. Atmospheric pressure and winds are important controls of climate. The pressure changes are the cause of the winds, and winds are the media by which heat is transferred between the high and low latitudes and moisture is transported from the oceans over continental areas.

WINDS RESULT FROM PRESSURE DIFFERENCES. *Wind* is defined as air that moves parallel to the earth's surface; *pressure* refers to the weight of the atmosphere. When air is cold and/or tends to descend from high altitudes toward the earth's surface, pressure is high; when air is warm and/or tends to rise, it weighs less and pressure is low. Pressure differences on the earth may also originate from dynamic causes such as the centrifugal force which accompanies earth rotation and from the friction which results from winds moving over different types of land surfaces. Winds blow *from* areas of high pressure *toward* areas of low pressure. The greater the differences in pressure the greater will be the velocity of the wind.

WIND AND PRESSURE BELTS. The heat that the earth receives from the sun and the deflective forces accompanying earth rotation contribute to a latitudinal arrangement of wind and pressure belts. This general pattern of belts or zones which we shall describe is not completely accurate for all parts of the earth's surface because of the different rate of heating and cooling of land and water bodies and various other conditions, but it does help to

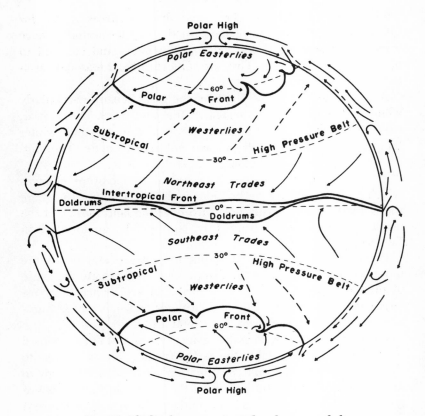

Fig. 17. Idealized pattern of wind and pressure belts.

explain why there are differences in climate on the earth. (See Fig 17.)

1. *The doldrum belt* is an area of calms, variable winds, and low pressure located in the very low latitudes. Temperatures are high during the entire year, winds converge toward this area from both the north and the south, and the major movement of air in this region is upward.

2. *The subtropical high pressure belts,* or "horse latitudes," lie in the vicinity of 30 degrees of latitude both north and south of the equator. In these zones air that has ascended to high altitudes from the doldrums has moved poleward and settles toward the earth as the result of cooling and the deflective force of earth

rotation. Winds diverge when they reach the earth's surface in the horse latitudes; part of the air moves toward the poles and part toward the equator. In these belts of settling air, surface winds are often absent or are light and variable.

3. *The trade wind belts* lie between the horse latitudes and the doldrums in both the northern and southern hemispheres. Air originates in the subtropical high pressure zone and moves toward the equator. Because of the deflective force of earth rotation[1] these winds are deflected to the right in the northern hemisphere and to the left in the southern hemisphere and blow from an easterly direction. Thus the trade winds, which are probably the most steady and regular winds of the earth, are also known as the tropical easterlies.

4. *The westerly wind belts* are located poleward of the horse latitudes. Air originates in the subtropical high, moves toward the poles, and deflection causes winds to blow from westerly directions in both hemispheres. Because of disturbances which will be described later, the westerlies are extremely variable in both force and direction. They continue poleward until they meet air moving equatorward from the poles in latitudes that vary with the season.

5. *The polar high pressure zones* result from the accumulation of cold, heavy, and settling air of the extreme high latitudes. They have high pressures, are areas of calm, and air moves outward from them toward the equator.

6. *The polar easterlies* are winds which originate in the polar high pressure belt and move equatorward. Since they are deflected by earth rotation, they blow from easterly quadrants. These winds do not blow with great velocity except when accumulations of cold air in the polar highs cause them to surge equatorward with gale-like force.

---

[1] The deflective force of earth rotation is known as *coriolis force*. This is an apparent force by which freely moving bodies over the earth are deflected to the right of the direction of motion in the northern hemisphere and to the left in the southern hemisphere. It is the result of the fact that the speed of earth rotation is greater in the equatorial areas than it is in the high latitudes. If this force were not present, low latitude winds would blow directly from the horse latitudes to the doldrums, or from north to south in the northern hemisphere.

7. *The subpolar low pressure belts* or polar fronts are discontinuous zones of rising and converging air which represent areas of contact between the westerlies and the polar easterlies. Usually they are belts of atmospheric disturbance and their location will vary from as much as 35 degrees to 65 degrees of latitude in the northern and southern hemispheres.

MODIFICATIONS OF THE WIND AND PRESSURE BELTS. The wind and pressure belts described above can be observed most clearly over the oceans during the spring and autumn, when they are in their average positions. However, there are two significant variations in the traditional wind belts.

1. Just as the direct rays of the sun migrate between the Tropics of Cancer and Capricorn as the earth revolves, the wind and pressure belts migrate in similar fashion during a twelve-month period. During the northern hemisphere summer the doldrums, the horse latitudes, and associated wind and pressure zones shift northward from five to ten degrees from their average location. Six months later, in the northern hemisphere winter and the southern hemisphere summer, the entire wind belt system has moved in the opposite direction. Therefore, those areas located near the margins of the various wind belts experience different winds at different seasons of the year. (See Fig. 18.) The wind belts lag behind the sun in this latitudinal migration, and the total shift is greater over continents than over oceans.

2. The more significant variation from the pattern of wind and pressure belts results from the different rate of heating and cooling of land and water bodies. In the middle latitudes, air over large continental land masses becomes greatly heated during the summer season. This warm-to-hot air tends to rise and in doing so draws winds in from all directions toward the center of heat, which is also the center of low pressure. During the winter season the reverse condition occurs: air over the continents becomes cold and heavy and moves outward in all directions from the center of cold and of high pressure. Ocean water heats up less rapidly in summer and cools off less rapidly in winter than does land, so the air over the ocean is relatively warm in winter and relatively cool in summer as compared to the air over the land. Thus, over large mid-latitude land masses like Eurasia and North America, the traditional wind belts are interrupted by winds which reverse

JANUARY

JULY

Fig. 18. Prevailing sea level wind direction. (COURTESY OF UNITED STATES NAVY DEPARTMENT, FROM *Aerology for Pilots.*)

their direction of movement between winter and summer and are called *monsoons.* (See Fig. 18.)

GENERAL CIRCULATION OF THE ATMOSPHERE. Many modern climatologists reject the traditional description of the world's wind systems outlined above as being inaccurate and interpret the circulation of the atmosphere in terms of oceanic whirls, polar outbursts, and certain other phenomena.

The pattern of prevailing winds at the surface of the earth is viewed as being dominated by giant *oceanic whirls* centered on the North and South Atlantic, the North and South Pacific, and the Indian Ocean basins (see Fig. 18). About each of these whirls there is a great high pressure cell of air which moves in a clockwise direction in the northern hemisphere and in a counterclockwise fashion in the southern hemisphere. In the northern hemisphere the air circulates from the south and west in a poleward direction along the western parts of the ocean basins and adjacent continents, crosses the high latitude seas from west to east, and returns equatorward along the eastern sides of the ocean basins and their coasts as winds from the north. The circulation of air in the three southern ocean basins is in the opposite direction and the winds in the low latitudes of both hemispheres move from east to west. This concept appears to recognize the existence of something like the doldrums, a series of subtropical high pressure cells, and a trade wind belt.

A second aspect of atmospheric circulation that is contained in this theory is related to the cold air that forms over polar icecaps and high latitude snow-covered surfaces. The chilled air is heavy and accumulates in huge masses which move equatorward at irregular intervals into areas of higher temperatures and lower pressure. These *polar outbursts* come in contact with the warmer air of the oceanic whirls, creating the fronts and cyclonic storms which bring changeable weather in the middle latitudes. This is the zone of contact which was described earlier as the subpolar low pressure belt or polar front.

The concept of oceanic whirls and polar outbursts requires two other elements to complete the pattern of the earth's atmospheric circulation. One of these is the *monsoons,* or seasonal shifts in wind direction, which interrupt the oceanic whirls on lower middle latitude east coasts; the other is the relatively recently discovered air movement known as jet streams. *Jet streams* are high velocity winds which move from west to east at high altitudes to the poleward of subtropical high pressure zones. They fluctuate considerably in their latitudinal position and appear to be the movement of air at high elevations away from the accumulations that have developed where polar outbursts have pushed into an oceanic whirl and forced a large volume of air upward. Jet streams sharpen the contrasts between polar and low latitude temperatures and appear to contribute much to the variable weather of the middle latitudes.

Air Masses and Storms.   Much of what has been described under the heading of wind and pressure belts and general circulation of the atmosphere is interpreted by meteorologists in terms of air masses and storms. An *air mass* is a large body of air that has uniform temperature and moisture characteristics. It has remained over a particular portion of the earth's surface long enough to develop properties that are derived from the surface upon which it rests. Areas where air masses develop are called *source regions* and an air mass carries the characteristics of its source region to other places. When two unlike air masses meet, the line of contact between them is called a *front*. Storms are churning movements of air which may originate along a front.

AIR MASSES. The classification of air masses is based upon the nature of their places of origin or source regions (see Fig. 19).

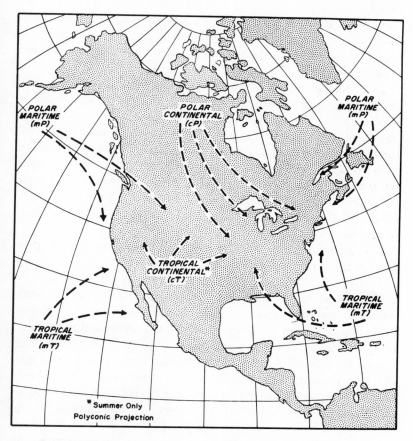

Fig. 19. North American air masses. (COURTESY OF UNITED STATES AIR FORCE, FROM AFM 105-5, WEATHER FOR AIRCREWS.)

Source regions are usually classified as polar (*P*) or tropical (*T*) and then subdivided into maritime (*m*) and continental (*c*). Further modifications (which will not be considered here) are the use of the letters *K* and *W* to indicate air masses that are colder or warmer respectively than the surface upon which they rest, and the use of the small letters *s* or *u* to indicate stable or unstable air with respect to its tendency to rise or not.

1. A polar continental (*cP*) air mass is one that has come from a cold continental source region. It is made up of chilled, heavy, dry air, and as it sweeps equatorward from its place of origin it may become a polar outburst and be associated with blizzardlike conditions. In terms of wind belts, a polar continental air mass may be considered to have originated in a polar high pressure zone and, as it moves equatorward, to constitute winds described as polar easterlies.

2. A tropical maritime (*mT*) air mass originates over warm ocean water and moves poleward. It consists of warm, light or buoyant air, and usually contains large amounts of water vapor. As one of these air masses moves over land in summer it may be further heated, be accompanied by hot humid weather, and be referred to as a *heat wave*. Subtropical high pressure areas over oceans are the sources of tropical maritime air masses and their poleward movement may become a part of the prevailing westerlies of the middle low latitudes. Air in the equatorward portions of oceanic whirls is tropical maritime.

3. Polar maritime (*mP*) air masses bring cool moist air to portions of the earth over which they pass.

4. Tropical continental (*cT*) air is hot and dry.

The nature of the several air masses may differ greatly from winter to summer because of the seasonal changes in the weather of their source regions. Tropical weather is controlled almost entirely by tropical air masses and there is little temperature change from day to day. Polar weather comes from polar air masses and although there is seasonal variation it is usually cool to cold. Mid-latitude weather is dominated in winter by polar air and in summer by tropical air, but weather changes may occur in any season as one type of air mass replaces another.

STORMS. Atmospheric disturbances or storms are centers of rising air which result from the convergence of two unlike air

CONVECTIVE THUNDERSTORM.

OROGRAPHIC THUNDERSTORM.

Fig. 20. Thunderstorms. (Courtesy of United States Air Force, from AFM 105-5, Weather for Aircrews.)

masses, from excessive heating of a portion of the earth's surface, or from winds being forced to rise over mountain barriers.
They bring weather changes and are the origin of the earth's
precipitation.

Thunderstorms. Thunderstorms are usually the result of high
temperatures on the ground causing columns of air to be thrust
violently aloft (see Fig. 20). Rising currents of air surrounded by
down-drafts cause a vigorous churning in the atmosphere which
produces heavy, but short duration, precipitation accompanied
by thunder, lightning, and sometimes hail. As the air rises it cools
to a temperature at which condensation takes place and the re-
lease of latent heat[2] with condensation stimulates still stronger
vertical movement. Storms of this type, known as *convective
thunderstorms,* provide much of the summer rainfall of the midlatitudes and a large part of the precipitation of the humid
tropics.

Thunderstorms also occur in mountainous regions where warm
moist air is forced to rise up a mountain slope. (See Fig. 20.)
Ascending air is cooled until condensation takes place and sufficient latent heat is released to cause excessive turbulence and the
formation of a thunderstorm. In this case the rising currents of air
are the result of winds rising up the mountainside instead of the
excessive heating described above. Storms of this type are usually
called *orographic thunderstorms.*

Mid-Latitude Cyclones and Anticyclones. A cyclone is an atmospheric disturbance which is characterized by winds moving
spirally in toward a center of low pressure. Cyclonic disturbances
are one of the most effective controls of weather and climate in
the middle latitudes.

Mid-latitude cyclones originate as wave-like disturbances along
the zone of contact between two unlike air masses (see Fig.
21)—which is the polar front or sub-polar low between polar and
tropical air masses. When air masses moving from opposite directions come in contact with each other, they do not blend together

---

2 Since heat is necessary for the evaporation of water, heat also must be
released during the condensation of water vapor. These changes of heat
energy are known as *latent heat of vaporization* and *latent heat of condensation,* respectively.

but indentations develop, with air from the south overtaking air from the north in one area and the cold northern air advancing over warm air in other areas. This air movement causes whirls to be set up, creating the spiral features which are common to cyclonic storms. The zone of contact between the two air masses (the front) has different weather conditions on either side and the entire storm, including both the low pressure center and the fronts, moves from west to east with the westerlies. Mid-latitude cyclones are nonviolent storms and are usually several hundred

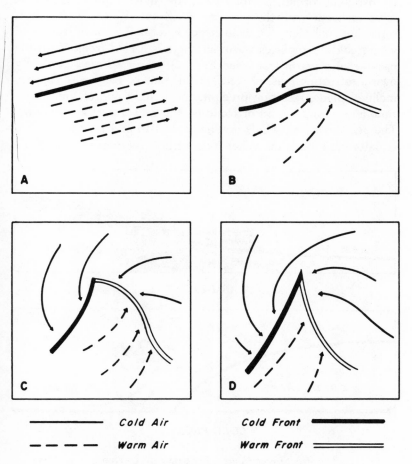

Cold Air ——————
Warm Air — — — —
Cold Front ▬▬▬▬
Warm Front ══════

Fig. 21. The growth of a cyclone.

miles in diameter. They travel in fairly well defined paths, in the upper middle latitudes in summer and in the lower middle latitudes in winter, at average speeds of 20 to 30 miles an hour.

The weather changes that take place with the passage of a mid-latitude cyclone depend upon the sector of the storm which moves across a particular place. The poleward portion of the cyclone consists of cold, heavy, and usually dry air and brings few changes in the weather. The equatorward sectors are composed of warm, light, and humid air which may easily be induced to rise and bring precipitation. The most rapid changes in weather occur with the passage of a front. Where warm air is replacing cooler air, the disturbance is termed a *warm front,* and where cold air replaces warm air there is a *cold front.* With the passage of a warm front (see Fig. 22), warm air rises gradually over a retreating mass of cold air, the zone of contact is a gently inclined plane, resulting precipitation is light and of long duration, and a long period of cloudiness and overcast skies follows. The accompanying winds gradually shift from a poleward to an equatorward direction. When a cold front passes over an area the

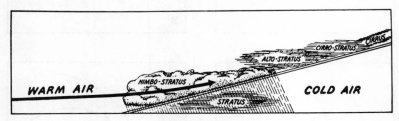

WARM FRONT.

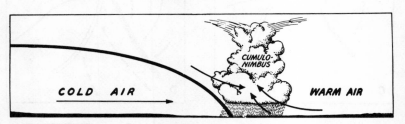

COLD FRONT.

Fig. 22. *The structure of fronts.* (Courtesy of United States Navy Department, from *Aerology for Pilots.*)

weather changes are more rapid. Polar air aggressively pushes into warm air and thrusts it violently upward. This air movement creates great turbulence in the atmosphere as evidenced by gale velocity winds, thunder and lightning, and heavy precipitation. The precipitation that accompanies a cold front, although heavy, is of short duration and the disturbance is very similar to that of a convective thunderstorm. With the passage of a cold front, the weather changes from warm, humid, and rising air with low pressure to cool, dry, settling air and high pressure.

Anticyclones are centers of high pressure which usually follow and precede cyclones. They are non-violent storms made up of air which moves spirally outward from a center of high pressure, clockwise in the northern hemisphere and counterclockwise in the southern hemisphere. They are generally clear weather areas.

Tornadoes and Hurricanes. Tornadoes are violent cyclonic storms which accompany a strong cold front in some parts of the middle latitudes. In the northern hemisphere these storms, sometimes called twisters, have winds which blow spirally, counterclockwise, and in toward a low pressure center. Tornadoes cover relatively small areas, have sharp pressure differences between their centers and outer margins, and have very high wind velocities. The destructiveness of these storms results from the high winds and from the explosive effect which accompanies very low pressure.

Hurricanes are tropical cyclones which are the result of the excessive heat and humidity of the low latitudes. They are low pressure storms which in many ways resemble tornadoes. Hurricanes seem to originate on the margins of the inter-tropical front and maintain themselves by heat of condensation. The destructiveness of the gale force winds is amplified by the great masses of sea water driven onshore by the high winds and by the floods resulting from the heavy rainfall.

Ocean Currents. Ocean currents follow closely the pattern of prevailing surface winds and have much the same effect upon climate in their areas as do those winds. However, their influence upon temperature and precipitation is sufficient to warrant their being considered major climatic controls.

THE DRIFT OF OCEAN WATERS. The direction of movement of water in the world's oceans is governed by the deflective force of earth rotation and the configuration of land masses, as well as by prevailing wind direction. In general, the circulation of ocean water is clockwise in the northern hemisphere and counterclockwise in the southern hemisphere. (See Fig. 41, page 172.) The drift of water in the equatorial zone is from east to west and in the higher latitudes is from west to east. The higher latitudes and east coasts of continents are bordered by warm waters moving poleward from the low latitudes; the west coasts of the lower latitudes are bordered by water that is cooler than the land. In certain areas there are countercurrents and small drifts of water which alter this general picture.

THE EFFECTS OF OCEAN CURRENTS. Ocean currents have their greatest influence upon land temperatures when the wind direction is from the sea toward the land. Where winds blow steadily from the sea to the land the effect of the ocean current may be considerable. If air moves over a cool stretch of water to warm land, precipitation is low; when the air moves across warm water to relatively cool land, precipitation is usually heavy.

Altitude. Although a mountain peak receives as much insolation from the sun as a lowland area, the air is thinner at the higher elevation and much of the heat received is quickly lost. Generally, an increase in altitude or elevation means a decrease in temperature. The vertical change in temperature from a lowland area in the tropics to the snow-covered peak of a nearby mountain is very much like that which occurs in a horizontal direction between the equator and the poles. Temperatures decrease about one degree Fahrenheit for each 300 feet of elevation.

Mountain Barriers. Mountains affect climate in three ways: their higher elevations result in lower temperatures, as mentioned above; atmospheric pressure is lower at great heights; and mountains have a barrier effect upon rain-bearing winds. The lower pressure of high elevations is of little consequence as a climatic control, but where winds are forced to rise over mountains the effect upon precipitation is considerable (Fig. 20, page 43). As winds containing appreciable amounts of water vapor are forced to ascend mountain slopes, they are cooled by the higher elevation, their ability to hold moisture is lessened, and heavy precipitation falls. When winds cross mountain crests in this manner and descend the other side, the temperature of the winds increases, they tend to retain moisture, and the result is dryness. Those mountain slopes which face the prevailing winds, known as *windward* slopes, are rainy and those facing the opposite direction, called *leeward* slopes, are dry. Leeward slopes are said to be in the *rain shadow* of mountains.

CLIMATIC ELEMENTS

Man perceives, describes, and analyzes atmospheric phenomena in terms of the climatic elements: temperature, precipitation, pressure, and winds. These four elements may differ widely from place to place, but they also may occur in the same general combination in areas which have broadly similar characteristics and are classified as climatic types.

Temperature. Temperature is the degree of heat or of cold and is measured by a thermometer marked in degrees Fahrenheit or Centigrade. Although the earth is some 93,000,000 miles from the sun and receives only a very small part of the energy which that body transmits into space, the sun is the only significant source of heat for the earth's atmosphere.

The climatic controls operating singly or in combination produce great differences in temperature over the surface of the earth. The most significant variations in temperature result from the influence of the climatic controls of latitude, altitude, and the distribution of land and water bodies.

Precipitation. The earth's atmosphere is a mixture of nitrogen, oxygen, hydrogen, carbon dioxide, water vapor, and several other gases. With the exception of water vapor, this mixture of gases is fairly constant. However, the amount of water vapor in the air, which is the source of the precipitation which falls upon the earth, varies widely.

HUMIDITY, DEW POINT, AND CONDENSATION. The moisture content of the atmosphere is understood in terms of *humidity*— relative, specific, and absolute.[3] The amount of water vapor that

---

[3] Relative humidity is defined as the ratio between the amount of water present in the air and the maximum amount the air can hold at a given temperature; absolute humidity is the amount of water vapor that a given volume of air contains expressed in weight per unit volume; specific humidity is mass (weight) of water vapor in a unit mass (weight) of air.

the air can hold varies with temperature: the warmer a given volume of the air the more moisture it can contain, and conversely, the colder the air the less moisture it retains. When a body of air contains all the moisture it can hold at a given temperature it is said to be *saturated*. The following table indicates the number of grains of water vapor a cubic foot of air can hold at various temperatures in degrees Fahrenheit:

Degrees Fahrenheit	90°	80°	70°	60°	50°	40°	30°
Grains of Water Vapor	14.9	10.9	8.1	5.7	4.1	2.8	1.9

When a mass of air is cooled, it may reach a temperature at which it becomes saturated, known as the *dew point*. If there is further cooling of the air, *condensation* takes place.

FORMS OF CONDENSATION. The several types of condensation result in six forms of conversion of water vapor.

Fog is like a cloud in contact with the earth. It occurs when warm moist air encounters a cool surface or when cool air comes in contact with a warm surface.

Dew is moisture which accumulates on plants and other objects when, after sunset, the earth rapidly loses sufficient heat to cause the temperature of the lower several inches of the atmosphere to drop below the dew point.

White frost is similar to dew and occurs when the dew point is below freezing (32° F.).

Hail occurs during thunderstorms and when there is great turbulence in the atmosphere. Hail is formed when rain is forced upward into very cold air and freezes as small ice pellets; when these ice pellets fall earthward from high altitudes, they pass through cold cloud layers, combine with other cold droplets, and then are forced upward again by rising currents of air. If this alternate rising and falling takes place several times, the hailstones acquire several layers of ice, grow larger, and finally fall to earth when their weight is greater than the lifting power of the updraft of air.

Rain and *snow* are the result of the coalescence of water droplets in clouds. Clouds form with the condensation of air at high altitudes. Water droplets in clouds are so light that they have insufficient weight to cause them to fall to the earth. The higher the humidity and the greater the cooling of cloud formations, the greater the amount of condensation. If the temperature is above freezing, rain falls to the surface of the earth; if the temperature is below 32° F., the condensation of water vapor results in snow.

CAUSES OF PRECIPITATION. When condensation results in moisture particles reaching sufficient size to fall freely in the atmosphere, precipitation takes place. Precipitation is caused by the excessive cooling of large amounts of air, and it occurs in significant amounts only in the form of rain or snow. There are three ways in which masses of air can be cooled sufficiently to bring about precipitation.

1. Convectional precipitation occurs when air is heated by contact with a warm earth and is forced to rise. As the air is forced upward it expands and cools. If the cooling is sufficient, condensation takes place and precipitation results.

2. Orographic precipitation results when a mass of air moves against a mountain range and is forced upward. As the air rises and is cooled, precipitation occurs.

3. Frontal precipitation takes place along the zone of contact, or front, between two air masses having unlike temperature and humidity characteristics. The cool air has greater weight and tends to cling to the earth while the warmer air is light and has a tendency to rise. If the warm air rises and cools sufficiently, condensation and precipitation will occur.

MEASUREMENT OF PRECIPITATION. Precipitation as rain is measured in inches with a rain gauge. Snow, hail, and other forms of precipitation are measured according to the amount of moisture they produce after melting. In studying the climate of a place or region, geographers are especially concerned with the average annual precipitation, the seasonal distribution of precipitation, and the reliability of precipitation.

Pressure. Although atmospheric pressure and winds are commonly included among the climatic elements, their significance is much less than that of temperature and precipitation.

Air pressure is measured by a barometer and is expressed in inches or millimeters. The slight pressure differences which occur at low elevations are seldom sensed by the human body. However, half of the atmosphere by weight is found below 18,000 feet in elevation and persons accustomed to life near sea level may experience great discomfort when flying in high altitude planes or when traveling in mountainous regions. The lower pressures of high altitudes and the accompanying low oxygen content of the atmosphere may cause nausea, dizziness, nosebleed, fatigue, and heart failure—an ailment known in some highland regions as *soroche*. Pressurized cabins and oxygen supplements are used in high altitude aircraft as protection against pressure differences.

Winds. Like pressure, winds in themselves are of minor importance as climatic elements, though they have great influence upon the principal climatic elements of temperature and precipitation. Although gale force winds may at times cause great damage to life and property in restricted areas, their significance as a climatic control is of much greater consequence on a worldwide scale than their importance as a climatic element.

Winds do have some effect upon human comfort or sensible temperatures. On a hot and humid day the movement of air causes evaporation of moisture from the skin and a loss of heat which makes a person more comfortable. Similarly, on a cold windy day personal discomfort may be increased by greater evaporation of moisture and heat loss.

Winds are indentified by the direction from which they blow— for example, a north wind blows *from* the north toward the south. The prevailing wind direction of a place is that direction from which the wind blows most often. Wind velocity or force is measured in miles per hour by an instrument called an anemometer. Velocities are frequently estimated by the use of a set of descriptive terms called the Beaufort Scale for Wind.

SUPPLEMENTARY READING

Aerology for Pilots. U.S. Navy, Bureau of Aeronautics, Training Division. New York: McGraw-Hill Book Co., Inc., 1943.

Blair, Thomas A., and Fite, Robert C. *Weather Elements.* 5th ed. Englewood Cliffs, N.J.: Prentice-Hall, Inc., 1965.

Blumenstock, David I. *The Ocean of Air.* New Brunswick, N.J.: Rutgers University Press, 1959.

Critchfield, Howard J. *General Climatology.* Englewood Cliffs, N.J.: Prentice-Hall, Inc., 1966.

Koeppe, Clarence E., and DeLong, G. C. *Weather and Climate.* New York: McGraw-Hill Book Co., Inc., 1958.

Trewartha, Glenn T. *An Introduction to Climate.* 3rd ed. New York: McGraw-Hill Book Co., Inc., 1954.

Weather for Aircrews. U.S. Air Force, Air Training Command, Air Force Manual No. 105-5. Washington, D.C.: Government Printing Office, 1962.

4

Climatic Types

The several controls of climate which were discussed in the preceding chapter cause wide differences in the climatic elements, and there are countless variations in climate over the surface of the earth. However, there are many regions of the globe which have similar precipitation and temperature characteristics, and these may be classified into general climatic types. The areas which have the same climatic type may be widely separated over the earth, but they have similar locations with respect to latitude and continental position. There is an observable system to the arrangement of climates on the surface of the earth which is reflected in the distribution of natural vegetation and soil types.

Various systems have been devised for the classification of climatic types. One system, based on the relationship between evaporation and precipitation, was devised by C. Warren Thornthwaite and consisted of five climatic groups or "provinces"—wet, humid, subhumid, semiarid, and arid. To each climatic group Thornthwaite assigned a rating for "precipitation effectiveness."

The most widely used scheme of classifying climates is that devised by a German meteorologist, Wladimir Köppen, in the early twentieth century. This system deals primarily with the two most important climatic elements, temperature and precipitation, and makes use of the long-time weather records that are available for places widely scattered over the earth. Since it utilizes numerical values of temperature and precipitation for determining the boundaries of climatic types, the method is both systematic and quantitative. Although numerous modifications of the original system have been proposed, it remains essentially as formulated over forty years ago.

CLIMATIC SYMBOLS OF THE KÖPPEN SYSTEM

The Köppen system employs letter symbols to define major types of climate. The characteristics of the climate of a place or area are expressed by a combination of two, three, or sometimes four letters. The first item in a classification is always a capital letter and designates a primary category; the letters which follow, usually lower case, designate the major subdivisions. The values of the most commonly used Köppen symbols are as follows:

A   Average temperature of coolest month 64.4° F. or over.[1]

B   Precipitation is exceeded by evaporation. Effectiveness of precipitation is determined by temperature. Formulas and tables have been established to show the boundary between dry and humid climates for various temperatures.

C   Temperature of coldest month between 64.4° F. and 26.6° F.,[2] average temperature of warmest month over 50° F.

D   Average temperature of the warmest month over 50° F. and of the coldest month under 26.6° F.[2]

E   Average temperature of the warmest month less than 50° F.

f   Humid throughout the year. When used with *A*, at least 2.4 inches of precipitation in all months of the year; when used with *C* or *D*, precipitation in the driest month of summer more than 1.2 inches,[3] precipitation in the driest month of winter more than 1/10th that of the wettest month of summer.

w   Dry season in winter. When used with *A*, at least one month in winter with less than 2.4 inches of precipitation. When used with *C* or *D*, precipitation in the driest month of winter less than 1/10th that of the wettest month of summer.

s   Dry season in summer. When used with *A*, at least one month in summer with less than 2.4 inches of precipitation. When used with *C* or *D*, precipitation in the driest month of summer less than 1.2 inches.[3]

m   Short dry season but very heavy precipitation during the remainder of the year. Used with *A*.

---

[1] The definitions presented here are based upon adaptations from W. Köppen, *Grundriss der Klimakunde* (Berlin, 1918 and 1931) and W. Köppen and R. Geiger, *Handbuch der Klimatologie* (Berlin, 1936), Vol. I.

[2] Many American geographers consider 32° F. to be a more useful value.

[3] The figure 1.6 inches is often used instead of 1.2 inches.

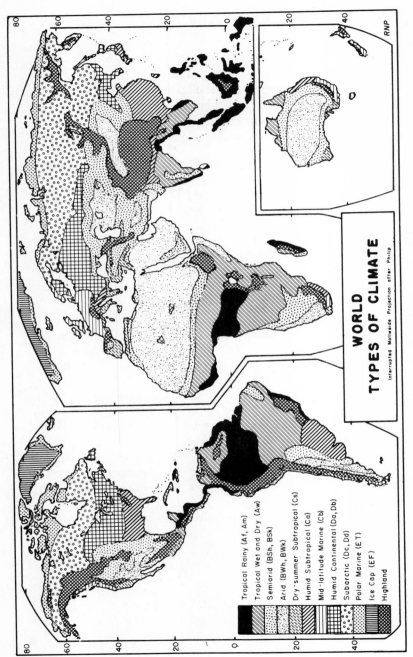

WORLD
TYPES OF CLIMATE

Interrupted Mollweide Projection after Philip

Tropical Rainy (Af, Am)
Tropical Wet and Dry (Aw)
Semiarid (BSh, BSk)
Arid (BWh, BWk)
Dry-summer Subtropical (Cs)
Humid Subtropical (Ca)
Mid-latitude Marine (Cb)
Humid Continental (Da, Db)
Subarctic (Dc, Dd)
Polar Marine (ET)
Ice Cap (EF)
Highland

RNP

Fig. 23.

a   Average temperature of the warmest month of the year over 71.6° F.

b   Average temperature of warmest month below 71.6° F. and at least four months with average temperatures over 50° F.

c   Average temperature of 50° F. or above for one to three months; average temperature of warmest month below 71.6° F.

S   Precipitation less than evaporation. Since effectiveness of precipitation is determined by temperature, the boundary between *S* and *A*, *C*, or *D* is computed according to established formulas. Used with *B*.

W   Annual precipitation less than half that separating *S* and a humid climate at the same temperature. Used with *B* only.

h   Average annual temperature over 64.4° F. Used with *B*.

k   Average annual temperature below 64.4° F. Used with *B*.

T   Average temperature of warmest month between 50° F. and 32° F. Used with *E*.

F   Average temperature of warmest month 32° F. or under. Used with *E*.

MAJOR TYPES OF CLIMATE

If the letter values of the Köppen system are applied to the data collected by weather stations, it is possible to divide the land areas of the world into a relatively small number of climatic types. Although many more might be recognized, the twelve climatic types described in the following paragraphs are usually considered to be sufficient for a basic classification of world climates. Since most of the readers to whom this volume is directed will not be required to memorize the definitions of letter symbols, descriptive terms are used to indicate major climatic types; the letter symbols which denote each are shown in parentheses. The location of the major climatic types is shown in Figure 23.

Rainy Tropical Climates (*Af*, *Am*). Rainy tropical climates are characterized by high temperatures and heavy precipitation in all months of the year; they lack seasonal variation. They are commonly regarded as being the most unhealthy and most unpleasant climates on the earth. Other terms which have been used to describe them are rainy tropics, humid tropical, tropical moist, and tropical rainforest.

Table 1

Climatic Data For Representative Stations

T., average monthly temperatures in degrees Fahrenheit.
P., average monthly precipitation in inches.

	J	F	M	A	M	J	J	A	S	O	N	D	Year
Iquitos, Peru (3°S., 73°W.)—Rainy Tropical													
T.	78	78	76	77	76	74	74	76	76	77	78	78	77
P.	10.2	9.8	12.2	6.5	10	7.4	6.6	4.6	8.7	7.2	8.4	11.5	103.1
Rangoon, Burma (16°N., 96°E.)—Rainy Tropical (monsoon phase)													
T.	77	79	84	87	84	81	80	80	81	82	80	77	81
P.	.2	.2	.3	1.4	12.1	18.4	21.5	19.7	15.4	7.3	2.8	.3	99.6
Kano, Nigeria (12°N., 8°E.)—Tropical Wet and Dry (No. Hemisphere)													
T.	72	77	85	89	88	83	80	78	80	81	78	73	80
P.	-	.1	.1	.5	2.5	4.8	8.2	12.1	5.5	.5	-	-	34.3
Cuiabá, Brazil (15°S., 56°W.)—Tropical Wet and Dry (So. Hemisphere)													
T.	81	81	81	80	78	75	76	78	82	82	82	81	80
P.	9.8	8.3	8.3	4	2	.3	.2	1.1	2.2	4.5	5.9	8.1	54.7
Khartoum, Sudan (15°N., 32°E.)—Arid (tropical)													
T.	73	75	81	81	93	93	90	88	89	89	82	75	84
P.	-	-	-	-	.1	.3	1.8	2.6	.7	.2	-	-	5.7
Santa Cruz, Argentina (50°S., 69°W.)—Arid (mid-latitude)													
T.	61	57	54	48	41	34	33	38	43	48	55	55	47
P.	.5	.3	.2	.6	.7	.4	1.1	.4	.2	.4	.4	1	6.2
Broome, Australia (18°S., 122°E.)—Semiarid (tropical)													
T.	86	85	84	83	76	71	70	73	77	81	85	86	80
P.	6.2	6.1	3.8	1.4	.6	.1	.2	.2	.1	.1	.1	3.7	22.6
Denver, Colorado (40°N., 105°W.)—Semiarid (mid-latitude)													
T.	30	32	39	47	57	67	72	71	62	51	39	32	50
P.	.4	.5	1	2.1	2.4	1.3	1.6	1.4	1	1	.6	.7	14
Los Angeles, California (34°N., 118°W.)—Dry Summer Subtropical													
T.	54	56	57	60	62	65	70	71	69	65	61	55	62
P.	3.2	3.3	2.6	1	.4	.1	-	-	.2	.5	1.1	2.4	14.8
Adelaide, Australia (35°S., 139°E.)—Dry Summer Subtropical													
T.	74	74	70	64	58	54	52	54	57	61	67	71	63
P.	.7	.8	1	1.7	2.7	3.1	2.6	2.4	2.1	1.7	1.1	.9	23.5
Montgomery, Alabama (33°N., 86°W.)—Humid Subtropical													
T.	48	51	58	65	73	80	82	81	76	66	56	49	66
P.	5.1	5.5	6.4	4.3	3.8	4.2	4.7	4.2	2.9	2.4	3.1	4.5	51.1

Data from H. Clayton, World Weather Records (Washington: The Smithsonian Institution, 1927); Climate and Man, Yearbook of Agriculture, 1941 (U.S. Department of Agriculture); W. Köppen and R. Geiger, Handbuch der Klimatologie (Berlin, 1930 and later); World Weather Records, 1941–1950 (Weather Bureau, U.S. Department of Commerce, 1959).

(Table 1, continued)

	J	F	M	A	M	J	J	A	S	O	N	D	Year

Buenos Aires, Argentina (34°S., 59°W.)—Humid Subtropical

	J	F	M	A	M	J	J	A	S	O	N	D	Year
T.	74	73	69	61	55	50	49	51	55	60	66	71	61
P.	3.1	2.7	4.4	3.5	2.9	2.5	2.2	2.5	3	3.5	3.1	3.9	37.3

Bergen, Norway (60°N., 5°E.)—Mid-latitude Marine (No. Hemisphere)

	J	F	M	A	M	J	J	A	S	O	N	D	Year
T.	34	34	36	42	49	55	58	57	52	45	39	36	45
P.	8.8	7.1	6.1	4.4	4.7	4.2	5.6	7.7	9.3	9.2	8.7	8.7	84.6

Puerto Montt, Chile (41°S., 73°W.)—Mid-latitude Marine (So. Hemisphere)

	J	F	M	A	M	J	J	A	S	O	N	D	Year
T.	60	58	56	52	50	46	46	46	47	51	54	57	52
P.	4.6	4.4	5.9	7.4	10.6	10	10.8	9.3	6.3	5.5	5.5	5.4	85.7

Columbus, Ohio (40°N., 83°W.)—Humid Continental, Warm Summer

	J	F	M	A	M	J	J	A	S	O	N	D	Year
T.	29	30	40	51	62	71	75	73	67	55	42	32	52
P.	2.9	2.1	3.4	2.7	3.1	3.3	3.5	3.2	2.6	2.4	2.2	2.6	34.1

Bucharest, Romania (44°N., 26°E.)—Humid Continental, Warm Summer

	J	F	M	A	M	J	J	A	S	O	N	D	Year
T.	27	33	42	52	62	69	73	72	64	54	41	34	52
P.	1.3	1.1	1.7	1.7	2.5	3.5	2.7	2	1.6	1.7	1.9	1.6	·23.3

St. Paul, Minnesota (45°N., 93°W.)—Humid Continental, Cool Summer

	J	F	M	A	M	J	J	A	S	O	N	D	Year
T.	12	15	28	46	58	67	72	70	61	48	31	19	44
P.	.9	.8	1.4	2.4	3.4	4.1	3.5	3.5	3.4	2.0	1.4	1.0	27.8

Moscow, U.S.S.R. (56°N., 37°E.)—Humid Continental, Cool Summer

	J	F	M	A	M	J	J	A	S	O	N	D	Year
T.	12	15	23	38	53	62	66	63	52	40	28	17	39
P.	1.7	.9	1.2	1.5	1.9	2	2.8	2.9	2.2	1.4	1.6	1.5	21.6

Dawson, Canada (64°N., 139°W.)—Subarctic

	J	F	M	A	M	J	J	A	S	O	N	D	Year
T.	−22	−12	4	28	46	57	59	54	42	26	1	−11	23
P.	.8	.7	.5	.6	.9	1.2	1.5	1.4	1.5	1.1	1.2	1.0	12.5

Yakutsk, U.S.S.R. (62°N., 130°E.)—Subarctic

	J	F	M	A	M	J	J	A	S	O	N	D	Year
T.	−46	−35	−10	16	41	59	66	60	42	16	−21	−40	12
P.	.9	.2	.4	.6	1.1	2.1	1.7	2.6	1.2	1.4	.6	.9	13.7

Barrow, Alaska (71°N., 156°W.)—Polar

	J	F	M	A	M	J	J	A	S	O	N	D	Year
T.	−20	−13	−13	−2	22	35	41	39	32	16	1	−15	10
P.	.1	.4	.2	.3	.3	.3	.9	.9	.5	.7	.3	.4	5.3

Svalbard (78°N., 14°E.)—Polar

	J	F	M	A	M	J	J	A	S	O	N	D	Year
T.	4	−2	−2	8	23	35	42	40	32	22	11	6	18
P.	1.4	1.3	1.1	.9	.5	.4	.6	.9	1	1.2	1	1.5	11.8

Bogota, Colombia (5°N., 74°W.)—Highland

	J	F	M	A	M	J	J	A	S	O	N	D	Year
T.	57	58	60	59	59	58	57	57	57	58	58	57	58
P.	2.0	2.2	2.2	4.4	4.2	2.2	1.5	1.7	1.9	5.1	3.8	2.9	34.1

Mexico City, Mexico (19°N., 99°W.)—Highland

	J	F	M	A	M	J	J	A	S	O	N	D	Year
T.	54	57	61	64	65	64	62	62	61	59	56	54	60
P.	.2	.2	.5	.8	1.9	3.9	4.5	4.6	3.9	1.6	.5	.2	22.8

Darjeeling, India (27°N., 88°E.)—Highland

	J	F	M	A	M	J	J	A	S	O	N	D	Year
T.	40	42	50	56	58	60	62	61	59	55	48	42	53
P.	.6	1.1	1.8	3.8	8.7	24.9	32.3	26.1	18.4	4.5	.8	.2	122.7

LOCATION. The rainy tropics extend across continents, except where interrupted by mountains, in belts bounded by latitudes of 5 to 10 degrees on either side of the equator. On windward coasts, usually eastern, they may reach as far poleward as 20 degrees. The most prominent areas of the world with this type of climate are found (1) in the Amazon Basin and along the east facing coasts of the low latitudes of Latin America, (2) in the Congo Basin and along the Guinea coast of Africa, and (3) in the East Indies and in some of the coastal portions of southeastern Asia.

TEMPERATURES. Areas in these extreme low latitudes have high temperatures in all seasons. By Köppen's definition, average temperatures are above 64.4° F. in all months. Typical stations, such as Iquitos and Rangoon (Table 1), show monthly averages [4] ranging from 74° to 87° F. Since there is a minimum of seasonal change, temperature differences between day and night are greater than between averages for the warmest and the coldest months. Extreme maximum temperatures seldom exceed 97° F. and extreme minimums generally do not fall below 65° F.

PRECIPITATION. Annual rainfall is heavy, with most places having in excess of 10 inches of rain during several months of the year. In some areas there are two short seasons with less rainfall, but places in this climatic type (Iquitos in Table 1) have 2.4 inches or more in each month—except those in the monsoonal (Am) subtype. Monsoonal areas have one, two, or more months with less than 2.4 inches (Rangoon in Table 1) but this is compensated for by very heavy precipitation for the remainder of the year. The heavy rainfall is caused by (1) the convectional currents of air which are the result of the high temperatures, (2) the convergence or frontal effects brought about by the meeting of trade winds from either side of the equator, and (3) orographic precipitation which occurs as winds which have passed across warm seas are forced to rise over mountains.

---

[4] The average temperature for a month is computed by first finding the mean daily temperature, which is the average of the high and the low for a twenty-four hour period; when the mean daily temperature is obtained for each day of a month the average for that month for that year can be computed; after monthly averages for a given year are obtained, they are included with others for the same months for as many years as weather records have been kept at that place.

RELATED ENVIRONMENTAL FEATURES. Climatic characteristics together with associated natural vegetation and soil types have produced a set of environmental conditions that make the tropical rainy regions generally unattractive to human settlement. Although modern science has done much to eliminate health hazards, the unproductive nature of the soils for cultivation and the rapidity with which obnoxious plants crowd out useful ones may cause many such areas to remain permanently underpopulated.

Natural Vegetation. Since there is no winter and no dry season, plant growth is both rapid and continuous. Vegetation is typically a dense forest of broadleaf evergreen trees called *selva*. Trees are large, the number of species is considerable, and in those areas with true rainy tropical conditions, the interlocking crowns of the trees block out the sunlight and prevent the development of a dense undergrowth on the ground. Where there is a short dry season, as in monsoonal areas, trees are farther apart and sunlight can reach the ground, and an impenetrable growth of bushes, vines, and shrubs covers the forest floor. The latter type of vegetation is often referred to as jungle.

Native Animal Life.[5] Native animal life is both varied and abundant; the most common types are the tree dwellers and those oriented toward streams. Large animals are not numerous but there are hundreds of species of reptiles, amphibians, and birds. Alligators, crocodiles, and many varieties of fish (some of which are flesh eaters) inhabit the streams; apes, monkeys, bats, and myriads of birds are found among the trees; and thousands of varieties of insects torment man and beast alike. Since there is no cool season the insects breed continuously; ants, termites, mosqui-

---

[5] The animal life of the world, although widespread and varied, does not correspond as clearly to climatic patterns as does natural vegetation. Plants are rather fixed in their environmental requirements and must adjust to them. Animals, on the other hand, are mobile and have the capacity to make some adjustment to environmental conditions. In the more heavily populated regions of the world most of the native animal life has been destroyed, but in areas where there are few inhabitants the fauna may provide subsistence commodities for primitive peoples or commercial quantities of fish or fur. Animals are commonly restricted to broad ranges, however, and secure their food directly or indirectly from local plants, so there is a rough correspondence of the distribution of animals to that of natural vegetation and climate.

toes, flies, leeches, and numerous others annoy human beings, attack buildings, and carry diseases.

Soils. Although one might expect differently because of the dense natural vegetation cover, residual soils in the humid tropics are generally not well suited to agriculture. Warm water soaking into the ground, or moving across the surface, chemically removes soluble salts and carries away fine particles, leaving soils that are high in insoluble minerals and coarse in texture. Reddish colors in the top soil are an indication of the presence of large quantities of iron and aluminum. Under hot and humid conditions, plant and animal organisms decay so rapidly after death that there is little accumulation of organic matter in the soil. Trees and deep-rooted plants can reach far enough beneath the surface to find the nutrients necessary for their sustenance, but the productivity of the soils for shallow-rooted crops is very low.

Tropical Wet and Dry Climate (*Aw*). The type of climate which borders the rainy tropics on their poleward sides has high temperatures throughout the year and one rainy season followed by one that is distinctly dry. Although the terms used to describe this climate usually involve the words "wet" and "dry," it is often designated by its principal vegetation type, *savanna.*

LOCATION. Tropical wet and dry climates extend across continents, except where interrupted by mountains, in belts located approximately between 5 and 20 degrees of latitude both north and south of the equator. They usually extend farther poleward on the eastern sides of continents. The areas of the world with this climatic type are usually referred to by the local names for tropical grassland or savanna. They are (1) the "llanos" of Venezuela and Colombia north of the equator in South America, (2) the "campos" of the interior of Brazil, (3) the "sudan" north of the equator in Africa, (4) the northern part of the "veld" south of the equator in Africa, (5) the northern part of Australia, and (6) a belt containing large parts of peninsular India, Burma, Thailand, and Cambodia in southern Asia.

TEMPERATURES. Average monthly temperatures throughout the year are over 64.4° F. (Kano, Nigeria, and Cuiabá, Brazil, in Table 1) but the slightly higher latitudinal position of this climate type gives a greater range of monthly averages and extremes of temperature than is found in the rainy tropical climates. Monthly averages may reach as high as 85° F. and extend below 70° F.; extremes vary from lows of around 55° F. to over 100° F.

PRECIPITATION. Regions in this type of climate are transitional between the rainy tropical and the arid tropical climates. During the high sun (warmer) period they have heavy rainfall like the rainy tropics, and the precipitation results from the atmospheric conditions described for that type of climate. During the low sun (less warm) period they resemble deserts; little or no precipitation occurs either because those regions come under the influence of the settling air of the subtropical high pressure belt, or because a shift in wind direction has put them on the leeward side of a mountain mass.

RELATED ENVIRONMENTAL FEATURES. The intermediate position of the wet and dry climate between regions that are continuously wet and those that are continuously dry makes it a transitional zone which has many features of rainy tropical forests along its equatorward margins and which merges into semiarid conditions on its poleward sides.

Natural Vegetation. The forests bordering equatorial regions gradually give way to areas of both forest and grass, and the latter give way to areas of grass and few trees as the amount of moisture for plant growth diminishes. Although few areas having this wet and dry climate are without trees, the year-round high temperatures and the long period without rain cause tropical grasses to predominate. In these "savannas," grasses are taller and trees are more conspicuous in the more humid, equatorward margins. Grass is shorter and trees are generally absent in the drier poleward portions, and the trees that are present tend to be small, widely spaced, and have adaptations which enable them to live through the long dry season. Where streams are present, the increased availability of moisture causes long tongues of *gallery forest* to penetrate into the savanna lands.

Native Animal Life. The wet and dry tropics support a varied and abundant animal life, but one that differs greatly from continent to continent. *Herbivores* such as the giraffe and zebra of Africa, the kangaroo of Australia, and various members of the antelope family feed upon grasses and the lower leaves of trees. The presence of a significant number of animals of this type provides sustenance for the flesh eaters (*carnivores*), such as members of the cat family, which prey upon them and upon each other. In addition, there are many scavengers, both animals and birds, that feed upon the remnants left by the carnivores. Numerous representatives of tropical forest fauna are found in the trees along the streams. Bird life is abundant and insects, including many insects of the rainy tropics, are present in large numbers.

Soils. Although relatively little is known about the soils of this type of climate, it can be assumed that they have many of the characteristics of those in the humid tropics. The chemical and mechanical removal of elements of fertility by water is a handicap and the accumulation of organic matter, although more favorable than in the tropical forests, is undoubtedly slow. Soils under this type of environment tend to be very sticky during the rainy season and very compact when dry.

Arid Climates (*BWh, BWk*). Arid climates (deserts) are those which suffer from an extreme lack of moisture. Although many types of arid climates may be recognized—among them are tropical, subtropical, and mid-latitude arid—they share the common characteristic that their annual precipitation is exceeded by evaporation, and therefore all types will be treated under one heading in this chapter.

LOCATION. Arid climates are usually found on the western sides of continents between 20 and 30 degrees of latitude, and they extend inland and poleward from this location to as far as 50 degrees of latitude. However, under the influence of cool ocean currents along the west coasts of South America and southern Africa, deserts in those areas reach much farther equatorward than is normally the case. The five broad regions of the world with arid climate are (1) an area extending inland from the west coast of northern Africa into east-central Asia which includes the Sahara, Arabian, Thar, and Gobi deserts; (2) the portion of North America which includes Lower California, the Sonoran Desert, much of the Mexican Plateau, the Colorado Plateau, and a large part of the Great Basin; (3) a belt extending from the north coast of Peru south to include the Atacama Desert of Chile, the zone lying east of the Andes of northern Argentina, and south to the Patagonian Desert; (4) the Kalahari Desert and adjacent areas of southwest Africa; and (5) the Great Sandy and the Great Victoria deserts of Australia.

TEMPERATURES. Since arid climates extend from the tropics well into the middle latitudes they have great differences in average and extreme temperatures. Variations occur in accordance with differences in latitude, altitude, and distance from the sea. Tropical deserts (*BWh*) have temperatures that are very similar to those found in other low latitude climates. (See Khartoum in Table 1.) Arid lands in the middle latitudes (*BWk*) have hot summers and cold winters. One feature common to all deserts, however, is the great diurnal range in temperature. Throughout the year in tropical deserts, and during the summer months in the middle latitudes, warm to hot days are often followed by cool nights. This wide daily variation is a consequence of the low water vapor content of the atmosphere. When the humidity is high, the heat that the earth receives from the sun, and radiates into the atmosphere, remains close to the earth. When there is little moisture in the air, this heat is quickly dissipated into space and after sundown, when the earth's surface is no longer receiving solar energy, there is a sharp drop in temperature.

PRECIPITATION. There are few areas in the world that are completely rainless, but low precipitation is the rule in all lands with arid climates. Even tropical areas with as much as 10 to 12 inches of rainfall may be classified as arid because the precipitation they do receive has little beneficial effect. In dry lands, rainfall averages have little meaning because of the great variation in amount from one year to another. A desert town may have all of its precipitation for a year in a single shower or it may be without rain for one or several successive years. A large part of the rainfall that does occur in such regions is of the thunderstorm variety. The lack of precipitation in arid regions is the result of their being located in parts of the earth where air is settling and being warmed. Such conditions are found in the subtropical high pressure belt on the leeward side of mountain barriers, and in the interior portions of large land masses.

RELATED ENVIRONMENTAL FEATURES. All aspects of the natural environment in deserts are strongly affected by the deficiency of moisture. Plant and animal life have special adaptations which enable them to exist through long periods of drought.

Natural Vegetation. Few desert regions are without some type of vegetation but in all instances plants do not completely cover the surface. The plants which are common to arid lands—bunch grass, cacti, dwarf trees, and bushes—adapt in one way or another to drought and high rates of evaporation. Thick bark, thorns, scanty foliage, waxy leaves, special water storage facilities, deep tap roots, extensive lateral root systems, and short life cycles are among the characteristics of desert plants which enable them to exist for long periods of time without water.

Native Animal Life. The harshness of the desert environment limits the number of species and the size of the animal population, but the paucity of animal life may be more apparent than real because many types are burrowers and nocturnal in character. Many have protective camouflaging coloration, and others depend upon swiftness of locomotion for protection. The herbivorous species that are present must be able to exist upon the scanty foliage and all must be able to survive for long periods of time without water. The camel, perhaps the most famous desert animal, has the most nearly perfect adjustment to the severe environment. Reptiles are numerous, but there are few birds.

Soils. The typical soils of deserts are low in organic materials, high in soluble minerals, and do not extend to great depth. The soils are usually grayish in color at the surface. In many places the presence of alkaline deposits precludes the existence of all but a few salt-tolerant plants, but elsewhere the addition of irrigation water may result in agriculture of high productivity.

Semiarid Climates (*BSh, BSk*). Surrounding deserts on all continents and separating them from humid climates are broad transitional zones that have semiarid climates. Since their one most prominent feature is short grass vegetation, these areas are often termed "steppe" climates.

LOCATION. Semiarid climates are found on all sides of deserts, except where deserts border the sea or an abrupt mountain front. They are broadest in extent in the interior plains of large continents where arid climates gradually merge into humid climates.

TEMPERATURES. As in deserts, temperatures in semiarid regions vary with latitude, altitude, and distance from the sea. Daily ranges of temperature are noticeable but the extremes are not so pronounced as in arid regions. Areas with this type of climate in the middle latitudes (Denver, Colorado, in Table 1) have a great range between summer and winter temperatures.

PRECIPITATION. Annual precipitation is higher than in deserts but it is still less than the evaporation potential. The climatic boundary between arid and semiarid areas is drawn where the annual precipitation is one-half that for the humid-semiarid boundary in the same latitude. Most of the rainfall is of the thunderstorm variety and there are noticeable differences in the total amount of precipitation from one year to another.

RELATED ENVIRONMENTAL FEATURES. The transitional nature of the semiarid lands is reflected in the natural vegetation, the native animal life, and the soil types. In each there is a gradation from types that are indicative of the deficiency of moisture to those which give evidence of an adequate supply of water.

Natural Vegetation. Short grasses, called steppes, are the predominant vegetation of semiarid climates. In addition to being generally short, the grasses are shallow rooted and tend to cluster in bunches giving an incomplete cover on the surface. The height of the grass and the extent to which the ground is covered at a particular location will depend upon the recency of the rainfall, the season of the year, and whether the place is situated closer to humid lands or to deserts.

Native Animal Life. The short grasslands of semiarid regions are the home of a variety of large grazing animals such as the wild horse, the gazelle, and the wild ass of central Asia; the bison of North America; and the guanaco of South America. Carnivorous animals such as the wolf, fox, and coyote are present, and there are numerous types of rodents. Snakes and lizards are common, as are flies, locusts, and grasshoppers in season.

Soils. The soils that develop under semiarid conditions and support short grass vegetation are gray to brown in color, relatively high in organic matter, and high in soluble minerals. They are of moderate to high fertility under irrigation, but when cultivated without supplementary water they soon exhaust their organic content, dry out, and become subject to wind erosion.

Dry Summer Subtropical Climates (*Csa, Csb*). Dry summer subtropical climates are characterized by a high percentage of sunshine in all seasons, by dry, warm-to-hot summers and mild, rainy winters. Since such conditions are most widespread in the borderlands of the Mediterranean Sea, the climatic type is often referred to as Mediterranean or Mediterranean subtropical.

LOCATION. Conditions similar to those in the Mediterranean Basin are generally found on the western sides of continents between 30 and 40 degrees of latitude, poleward from deserts. Because mountains are located close to the sea on most large land masses in these latitudes, dry summer subtropical climates seldom extend far inland. Five areas of the world have the climatic conditions and the location described above. They are (1) the borders of the Mediterranean Sea extending in a clockwise manner from Tunisia in North Africa through southern Europe and as far as Israel, and the margins of the nearby Black and Caspian Seas; (2) the coastal region of California from San Diego to San Francisco, and most of the Great Valley of California; (3) the central part of Chile; (4) the southwestern tip of Africa; and (5) two southern portions of the Australian continent, near Perth and near Adelaide.

TEMPERATURES. Summers are warm-to-hot with monthly averages extending from 65° to 73° F. (Los Angeles and Adelaide in Table 1) but at inland locations the temperature may reach as high as 100° F. Average temperatures for the coldest month are usually between 35° and 55° F. Frost and snowfall may occur during the winter season, although snow is unusual. Latitudinal location and nearness to the sea are the most important temperature controls.

PRECIPITATION. Mediterranean climates are transitional between deserts and mid-latitude humid types; their most equatorial parts are very similar to semiarid climatic regions. Dry sunny summers are characteristic of all areas having this climate type. Practically all precipitation comes during the winter at irregular intervals when the migration of the wind belts causes the prevailing air movement to be from a westerly, or off-shore, direction and when cyclonic storms which bring frontal and orographic precipitation reach these latitudes.

RELATED ENVIRONMENTAL FEATURES. The natural environment of the Mediterranean subtropical climate has many features similar to those of arid and semiarid regions.

Natural Vegetation. The typical vegetation cover is an evergreen forest of species of small trees and bushes that are adapted in one way or another to dryness. Woody plants tend to be small in size and widely spaced, to have thick bark and small waxy leaves, and to have either very deep or widely distributed root systems. Coarse types of bunch grass are common in some areas, particularly in California. During the winter season the earth is likely to be mantled with brilliantly green grasses and shrubs, but during the long dry summer the landscape is brown and parched.

Native Animal Life. The animal life of the dry summer subtropical climates lacks distinctive characteristics. Man has inhabited the shores of the Mediterranean Sea for so many centuries that it is difficult to reconstruct what was the original animal life there. In other areas having this climate type, the native animal life is transitional between the neighboring arid and humid regions, probably more like the former.

Soils. Since there are few extensive areas of level land in regions having Mediterranean climates, no typical soil characteristics have evolved. The soils of lower mountain slopes are naturally thin and are continuously being subjected to erosion, while on the narrow plains the frequent additions of alluvium preclude any uninterrupted period of soil development. Like the level lands of deserts, however, the lowland soils may be very productive when subjected to irrigation agriculture.

Humid Subtropical Climates (*Caf, Caw*). The eastern sides of continents, and their immediate interiors, in the lower middle latitudes have hot summers, mild winters, and abundant precipitation which is concentrated in the warm season. Areas having these characteristics are classified as humid subtropical.

LOCATION. Humid subtropical climates are found on the eastern sides of continents and in the east-central interiors of continents extending from latitudes of about 25 degrees poleward to 35 or 40 degrees. Such areas are found in the southeastern United States from Texas east to North Carolina and Florida; in southeastern China, southern Japan, and northern India in Asia; in that portion of South America which includes northeastern Argentina, southern Paraguay, southern Brazil, and Uruguay; along the Natal coast of southern Africa; and in the east-central coastal region of Australia.

TEMPERATURES. Latitudinal location causes this type of climate to have mild winters and warm-to-hot summers. Average monthly temperatures of 75° to 80° F. are common in summer (Montgomery, Alabama, and Buenos Aires, Argentina, in Table

1) and inland from the coast extremes in excess of 100° F. are not unusual. Although winters are generally mild, average temperatures vary from 35° to 50° F. and frosts occur frequently. Temperatures of this climate type are somewhat like those of dry-summer subtropical climates but extremes are noticeably greater. Monsoon winds bring outbursts of cold polar air to the humid subtropics in winter and moist hot air from the tropics in summer. In summer, the long daylight period under the almost direct rays of the sun also contributes to the high temperatures.

PRECIPITATION. Precipitation is abundant. The annual amount varies from 35 to 65 or more inches, and it is either well-distributed throughout the year or there is a distinct warm season maximum. Many humid subtropical lands are affected on their equatorward margins by monsoonal conditions which bring excessive summer rainfall. Some areas experience hurricanes or typhoons in late summer and autumn which may cause average annual precipitation to be higher than usual and may contribute to a secondary maximum precipitation period at that time of the year. The average abundant rainfall is brought by cyclonic storms which occur throughout the year, and the summer maximum precipitation is the result of the convectional thunderstorms which are caused by the excessive heating of the land.

RELATED ENVIRONMENTAL FEATURES. Located between lands that are continuously warm and those with pronounced winter seasons, the humid subtropical climates provide admirable conditions for a wide range of biological life.

Natural Vegetation. Although trees by far predominate in the vegetation cover, there is a considerable variety of plant life. Broadleaf forests are the most widespread vegetation type; on equatorial margins the forest is evergreen but elsewhere the trees lose their leaves during the short winter season. Coniferous growth is usually intermingled with broadleaf forests. The mixed subtropical forests gradually give way to grasslands on their drier western margins, particularly in the southern United States and in northern Argentina.

Native Animal Life. In those portions of the humid subtropics which have a large human population, especially in the Far East, native animal life has largely disappeared. Areas with relatively low population density have an abundant and varied animal life.

In the southeastern United States, until recent times deer, bear, fox, rabbits, squirrels, opossum, and raccoon were common, and birds of many species and sizes abounded. The animal population of the southern hemisphere humid subtropics is similar to that of the northern hemisphere, but is somewhat less varied and abundant. The woodland kangaroo in eastern Australia and a short-horned buffalo in southeastern Africa are types not found north of the equator. Swamps and marshes in most humid subtropical areas contain several species that are valuable for their hides and skins.

Soils. In the more humid portions of this type of climate the soils resemble those of the rainy tropics but are of higher fertility. The predominant colors of the soils are red and yellow, indicating a high content of iron and aluminum; the amounts of other soluble minerals and organic matter that are present are relatively low. Toward the drier margins of the humid subtropics, under the climatic conditions which have given rise to grasslands, the soils take on a dark brown color, are high in both soluble minerals and organic matter, and are usually of high fertility.

Mid-latitude Marine Climates (*Cb*). In many coastal regions of the middle latitudes, particularly west coasts, the climate is characterized by mild winters, cool summers, and abundant precipitation. Although this truly maritime climate, free from extremes, is designated here as mid-latitude marine, it may often be referred to as west coast marine or temperate marine.

Location. Mid-latitude marine climates are commonly found on the western sides of continents extending from 40 degrees of latitude poleward to 60 degrees. The west coasts of large land masses in these latitudes usually are backed by high mountain ranges, and this type of climate is therefore limited to fairly narrow coastal regions. However, in the lowland parts of western Europe, marine climate does extend inland a considerable distance. Mid-latitude marine climate covers extensive areas of the west coast of North America from northern California to Alaska, the coasts and islands of southern Chile, parts of the extreme southern portions of Africa and Australia, the island of Tasmania, and the islands of New Zealand.

Temperatures. Proximity to the sea and prevailing off-shore winds make this one of the most temperate of all climates; it is free from excessive heat in summer and winters are unusually mild for the latitude. Typical stations (Bergen, Norway, and Puerto Montt, Chile, in Table 1) have average monthly temperatures ranging from 55° to 60° F. in summer and from 35° to 45° F. in winter. Although there may be a few hot days during the summer season and cold spells in winter, the extremes in temperature are very moderate. In Seattle, Washington, for example, during a period of over forty years the extreme high temperature recorded was 98° F. and the absolute minimum was 3° F.

PRECIPITATION. Although there is considerable variation in amount of precipitation they receive, mid-latitude climates are universally well-watered. In basins or enclosed valleys the average annual precipitation may be as low as 30 inches per year but on mountain-rimmed coastlines it is frequently in excess of 80 inches. Heavy fogs are characteristic of coastal areas. Precipitation results from both orographic and frontal causes. Lying in the paths of cyclonic storms and westerly winds, these areas receive precipitation in all seasons, much of it in winter in the form of snow. During the winter months the waters offshore are relatively warm in relation to adjacent continents. Thus the condensation which results from winds blowing from over warm ocean waters onto cool land is a major factor in giving a winter maximum of precipitation.

RELATED ENVIRONMENTAL FEATURES. Climatic conditions along west coasts in the middle latitudes are considered maximum for human comfort and energy. The long growing season and abundant moisture favor the development of forests but do not always facilitate the formation of fertile soils or encourage crop agriculture.

Natural Vegetation. The mild and humid conditions which prevail throughout the year encourage a thick growth of forests. The density of the forest growth and the size of the trees vary with the amount of precipitation. In some areas the vegetation cover consists mainly of broadleaf deciduous species, but the west coast of North America has one of the world's finest stands of coniferous forests.

Native Animal Life. The native animal population of the mid-latitude temperate climates is not particularly abundant or specialized. There are undoubtedly more species and greater numbers in the northern than in the southern hemisphere. Many of the more numerous types are found in other climates as well; for example, in North America common representatives of the animal kingdom are the deer, bear, fox, rabbit, wolf, beaver, otter, badger, and squirrel.

Soils. The quality of the soil in these environments depends greatly upon the specific nature of the vegetation cover as well as upon minor climatic conditions. Generally, soils of the areas of broadleaf forest have higher organic content, greater mineral content, and higher fertility than those which are covered by needle-bearing trees. In many narrow strips of plain and foothills between the shorelines and mountains, typical soil types have never had the opportunity to develop because of excessive erosion and subsequent deposition.

Humid Continental Climates, Warm Summer Phase (*Daf, Daw*). On the eastern sides and eastern interiors of continents in the middle and upper middle latitudes, almost entirely within the northern hemisphere, the climates are not greatly affected by tropical or maritime conditions. They are characterized by great differences between summer and winter temperatures, have changeable weather in all seasons, and have adequate precipitation for crop agriculture. The dominant controls of the humid continental climates are continental position and cyclonic storms. Because of the striking differences between the equatorward and the poleward portions of this climatic zone in North America, it is a common practice among geographers to recognize warm (or long) and cool (or short) summer subdivisions.[6]

The humid continental, warm summer zone of the United States is often said to have the "Corn Belt" type of climate. It has long hot summers, and winter temperatures frequently drop below zero (0° F.).

LOCATION. The largest area having the warm summer phase of humid continental climate is found in the east central United States between 35 and 45 degrees of latitude. This belt extends

---

[6] On the map of world types of climate (Fig. 23, page 56), no attempt has been made to distinguish between the warm summer and cool summer aspects of humid continental climates.

east from central Nebraska and Kansas to the Atlantic Coast in the vicinity of New York City. There are smaller areas having the same general climate characteristics in the Danubian Plain of southern Europe and in eastern Asia, including portions of Manchuria, northern China, and Korea.

TEMPERATURES. In this climate, the long, often hot summers are followed by short, often cold winters. The continental interiors heat up greatly in summer and cool off markedly in winter, and therefore there are extremes of temperature throughout this climate zone, depending upon the latitudinal location of places. Cyclonic storms bring variable spells of weather in all seasons. Monthly temperatures average 70° to 75° F. in summer and 25° to 30° F. in winter (Columbus, Ohio, and Bucharest, Romania, in Table 1). However, in such places as Columbus, or St. Louis, Missouri, or Peoria, Illinois, the thermometer usually rises above 100° F. for several days in summer and temperatures of 5 to 10 degrees below zero in winter are not uncommon. The growing season is at least 130 days in length and in some areas may last for 180 days.

PRECIPITATION. Most areas have adequate but not excessive precipitation; the total rainfall averages around 25 to 35 inches annually. Frontal type rainfall associated with the passage of cyclonic storms is the source of most of this precipitation, although convectional thunderstorms occur frequently in summer. Much of the winter precipitation is in the form of snow and the earth's surface may be snow-covered for several weeks at a time during the cool season. In broad areas having this type of climate, the amount of precipitation is greatest at the coast and decreases toward the continental interiors; the interior areas then become part of a wide transitional zone with semiarid climate.

RELATED ENVIRONMENTAL FEATURES. Within humid continental climates, the considerable variation in environmental features is related to the transition from mild to severe winters and from humid coasts to semiarid continental interiors.

Natural Vegetation. The mixed forests of the humid subtropics continue poleward into humid continental areas and there is a corresponding change to tall grass (prairie) vegetation toward the drier continental interiors. Broadleaf deciduous forests are found in the areas with the more favorable soil and slope conditions, and coniferous forests are present elsewhere. Since amounts of precipitation decrease inland, the grasslands which are interspersed with the prevailing woodlands become broader in extent until in the humid/semiarid border zone trees are present only along streams and in other places where there is sufficient moisture for their growth.

Native Animal Life. Although the native animal life in the forested sections of these climates differed considerably from that in the grassland portions, it was undoubtedly varied and abundant in both. Since such areas have long been occupied by sedentary peoples, the wild animal life of today is of little significance in considering the habitability of these areas.

Soils. The residual soils which are present under the climatic and vegetative conditions described above are of moderate to high fertility and generally vary in accordance with the amount of precipitation. In the more humid portions of this climate zone, the surface soil is gray to brown in color and it stands up well under types of agriculture which provide for the maintenance of soil fertility. In the grassland portions the soils are dark brown to black in color, are high in organic content and soluble minerals, and are generally highly productive.

Humid Continental Climates, Cool Summer Phase (*Dbf, Dbw*). The cool, or short, summer phase of humid continental climates has general characteristics which are much like those described for the warm summer phase; the major differences are the result of the higher latitudinal location.

LOCATION. The two large areas of the world with humid continental, cool summer characteristics are found (1) in the northeastern and north central United States and adjacent portions of Canada, and (2) in a belt extending from Poland and central European Russia inland into central Siberia. A smaller area is found in eastern Siberia, northern Manchuria, and northern Japan. Latitudinal position is between 45 and 55 degrees in North America and north to 60 degrees in Eurasia. This climatic type is not found in the southern hemisphere.

TEMPERATURES. Winters are colder and longer than in the warm summer phase. Average monthly temperatures range from 10° to 15° F. in winter (St. Paul and Moscow in Table 1) and from 65° to 70° F. in summer. There may be short periods of hot weather in the summer months, and several weeks with below zero temperatures are typical of the winter season. Changeable weather is likely to occur in all seasons, particularly in spring and autumn. The relatively short growing season (120 to 100 days) imposes serious limits upon agriculture.

PRECIPITATION. With regard to precipitation, there is little to distinguish cool summer from warm summer humid continental climates. The cool summer phase has less convectional rain in summer; snowfall is somewhat heavier and the earth's surface is covered with snow throughout most of the winter months. There is the same decrease in precipitation accompanying an increase in distance from the sea.

RELATED ENVIRONMENTAL FEATURES. The other features of the natural environment are very similar in the warm summer and cool summer humid continental areas. However, the long cold winters of the cool summer phase have considerable influence upon biotic life and soils, causing many characteristics which are more common to subpolar areas to appear.

Natural Vegetation. Although broadleaf deciduous forests are the major vegetation type, coniferous trees are more common than in the warm summer regions and on the poleward margins the conifers predominate. The shorter summers and the long cold winters make it more difficult for species such as oak, hickory, and maple to compete with pine, spruce, and fir. As in the warm summer phase, forests give way to grasslands toward drier continental interiors.

Native Animal Life. Over much of the cool summer areas the native wild animal life has been displaced by advancing civilization. Toward the colder portions of those areas, where population density is lower, many animals associated with subpolar regions are numerous—deer, moose, bear, beaver, otter, and rabbit.

Soils. Generally speaking, the soils follow the pattern set by other environmental features. They are like those of areas with humid continental warm summer climates but toward the north become increasingly similar to those of the subarctic lands, described below.

Subarctic Climates (*Dfc, Dwc*). The great northern forest belts of North America and Eurasia are regions of long cold winters, brief summer seasons, and great extremes of temperature.

Climatic features have such a strong control over other elements of the natural landscape that there is considerable correspondence among climatic, vegetation, and soil boundaries. What is termed subarctic here may also be known as polar continental, boreal forest, or northern coniferous forest climate.

LOCATION. The subarctic belts stretch across the northern portions of the great land masses of the northern hemisphere between the Atlantic and the Pacific Oceans. Except for a few isolated areas, the subarctic climates are not found on the coasts bordering the Arctic Ocean. Because of the westerly drift of air and warming ocean influence in the upper middle latitudes, these subarctic belts extend farther poleward on the western sides of continents and farther equatorward on the eastern sides.

TEMPERATURES. Long cold winters are characteristic of subarctic climates. Location in the upper latitudes and distance from moderating seas cause many areas (Dawson, Canada, and Yakutsk, U.S.S.R., in Table 1) to have seven or more months each year with average temperatures below freezing. In the winter season the nights are long and during the daylight period the sun's rays strike the earth at such an oblique angle that their heat is not very effective. In the winter months temperatures often reach –50° F. and thermometer readings of –90° F. have been recorded. During the brief summer period, when there are three months or less with average temperatures above 50° F., the days are long and spells of quite warm weather may be experienced. Although the sun's rays are never very direct even in the summer season, the duration of the daylight period, which is 20 hours or more in some places, may cause maximum temperatures of 80° to 90° F. The short growing season, less than 90 days in most places, handicaps plant growth and is a factor in the relative unimportance of agriculture.

PRECIPITATION. Contrary to popular opinion, snowfall is not universally heavy in subarctic climates and precipitation is generally light, normally less than 20 inches per year. The northlands are areas of cold, settling, outward moving air which tends to hold off rainbearing winds blowing from warmer regions. In addition, the low temperatures of those climates are accompanied by low humidity. Most of the precipitation takes place during the warmer months and is usually frontal in origin.

RELATED ENVIRONMENTAL FEATURES. Maps showing the distribution of major climatic types, vegetation zones, and soil groups reveal that there is a remarkable similarity between the environmental features of the northern portions of the two great land masses of the northern hemisphere.

Natural Vegetation. In the subarctic climates the short growing season with relatively low temperatures is unfavorable for the growth of broadleaf trees, and the vegetation is primarily a coniferous forest (taiga). Compared to the forests of the middle and low latitudes the number of species is small, with spruce, fir, larch, and pine probably most widespread. Small stands of birch, poplar, willow, and a few other deciduous types may be found in areas that are more favorable for plant growth. In general, the short cool growing period retards tree growth.

Native Animal Life. The northern coniferous forests are the home of large numbers of animals, many of them valued for their fur pelts. Reindeer, moose, elk, bear, and wolves are typical animals of the forests; beaver, otter, muskrat, and mink are found in the swamps and marshes; there are great flocks of birds in summer; and trout, pike, and other types of game fish inhabit the lakes and streams. No description of the fauna of these lands would be complete without mention of the swarms of mosquitoes, gnats, and black flies which annoy men and animals alike during the summer season.

Soils. The climatic conditions and the vegetation cover of the subarctic regions do not favor the development of fertile soils. The coniferous trees provide little potential organic matter for the soil and the low temperatures retard its decay. Beneath the undecomposed needles, cones, twigs, and branches which cover the forest floor the top layer of the soil is light and friable, grayish in color, and of low fertility. Poor drainage conditions are widespread and many areas are further handicapped by a permanently frozen subsoil.

Polar Climates (*ET, EF*). The climates of the Arctic and Antarctic regions produce a harsh environment that sharply restricts human activity. As in the tropics, the climate is monotonous, but in the polar climates the lack of variability results from the insufficiency of, rather than a prevalence of, warm weather. Statistical climatology recognizes two types of polar climate, polar marine and icecap, but in both types the weather is so severe that there is little reason for making a distinction between the two here.

LOCATION. The borderlands of the Arctic Ocean in the northern hemisphere and the continent of Antarctica in the southern hemisphere have a polar climate of severe cold, without a real summer season. Since the Arctic high latitude region is largely a body of water and Antarctica is an ice-covered land mass, there are great differences in climate between the two hemispheres, the most noticeable being the uniformity and the austere simplicity of climate which is found in Antarctica. Polar climates extend south of the 60th parallel in Canada east of Hudson Bay, and to approximately 60 degrees of latitude in eastern Siberia.

TEMPERATURES. The earth's revolution, combined with inclination and parallelism of the earth's axis, causes the polar regions to have very long days and short nights in summer, and long nights followed by short days in winter. Theoretically the poles have six months of daylight followed by six months of darkness. The sun is never more than 23½ degrees above the horizon within the Arctic and Antarctic Circles, and therefore much of the polar areas receives almost no heat from the sun in winter and very little during the short summer season. The equatorward boundary of polar climates is fixed at the point where there is one month when the temperature averages 50° F., but over large areas of the polar regions there is no place where the average temperature is above freezing for one month. The regions along the shores of the Arctic Ocean may have a few warm days each summer and may have winter temperatures that are higher than in subarctic climates (see Barrow, Alaska, and Svalbard, in Table 1) but large areas of land are continuously cold and ice-covered.

PRECIPITATION. For the same reasons described for subarctic climates, polar maritime and icecap climates have light precipitation. Some moisture-carrying winds may reach coastal polar regions, but on the whole both rainfall and snowfall are light. Yet much of the polar land and ice surface is snow-covered even in summer because the year-round low temperatures permit very little melting.

RELATED ENVIRONMENTAL FEATURES. Since practically all of Greenland and Antarctica, and several other islands, are covered with glacial ice, the natural vegetation, animal life, and soils of the polar climate are of significance only along the Arctic shores of Canada, Alaska, and Siberia.

Natural Vegetation. The most widespread vegetation cover (called *tundra*) consists of grasses, mosses, shrubs, lichens, and flowering plants. Dwarf trees and bushes are found along the margins of the subarctic forest, but the polar icecaps are bordered by barren rocky surfaces. Low temperatures, very short frost-free seasons, and permanently frozen subsoils severely handicap plant growth even in the southern portions of the polar climates.

Native Animal Life. Land animals must have some type of adaptation such as thick fur or layers of protective fat to be able to survive in the harsh environment of the polar lands. The musk ox, certain types of fox and rabbit, and the polar bear are permanent inhabitants of the polar regions, but other animals, such as reindeer and wolves, migrate in from the subarctic forests during the summer months. The ptarmigan and other birds that dwell in these lands throughout the year are joined by many other species during the short warmer season. The seas which border the polar lands are teeming with life—whales and seals, and fish such as cod, salmon, and halibut. Just as in the subarctic regions, insects can be a problem during the summer months.

Soils. No well-developed soil types exist in the polar regions. Since the subsurface layers are permanently frozen, soil development is hindered, and imperfect drainage results in broad areas of swamp and marsh during the summer months.

Highland Climates. From the standpoint of uniformity of temperature and precipitation characteristics, there is no such thing as a highland or mountain type of climate. Sharp differences in elevation and in exposure to winds and sunlight cause any highland region to have a great variety of climatic features. On a journey from sea level to the crest of a mountain peak in the tropics one would encounter many of the climatic changes that one would meet on a trip taken at sea level from the equator to a polar icecap. Mountain climates are classified as being different from others on the basis that places with like temperature and precipitation are so small and so intricately distributed that it is virtually impossible to map them on a world scale. Some writers recognize this problem by referring to the climates of mountainous regions as "undifferentiated highland."

LOCATION. The main criterion that is used to separate mountains from other surface forms is significant vertical differentiation of temperatures. Thus the distribution of mountain climates corresponds to that of mountain ranges. The major highland regions of the world extend in four directions from the great mountain complex of central and southeastern Asia. One branch extends northeastward through northern China and eastern Siberia to join with the Alaskan highlands and continues southward to include an almost continuous chain of mountains along the western sides of both North and South America. The second extends south through southeast Asia and the East Indies to eastern Australia and New Zealand and, together with the highlands of the western hemisphere, forms a broken rim of mountains around the Pacific Basin. The third branch extends west from south central Asia across southern Europe and northeast Africa, and the fourth consists of a discontinuous system reaching from Ethiopia to the extreme southeastern part of Africa. Aside from this arrangement, truly mountainous areas occur only in scattered small areas of northern Africa, eastern North America, and eastern South America. Because of the great contrast between the climates at the foot and at the crest of mountains in the tropics, and because of their attractiveness to settlement, highland climates are more conspicuous in low latitudes than in the middle or high latitudes.

TEMPERATURES. Vertical differentiation of temperature is the principal feature of the climates of mountainous areas. An average temperature decrease of 3.5 degrees for each 1,000 feet of elevation causes temperatures of upper and middle mountain slopes to be significantly lower than those at sea level. This can be illustrated by the difference between the average monthly temperatures of Bogota, Colombia, and Iquitos, Peru (Table 1); both are in the tropics but Bogota lies at an altitude of 8,700 feet and Iquitos at 350 feet. In the low latitude mountains, the same monotony of temperature exists as is found at sea level; the difference is that the mountain temperatures are lower in all months. Mountainous areas outside of the equatorial zone, such as Darjeeling at an altitude of 7,400 feet and Mexico City at 7,500 feet, experience distinct seasonal weather changes.

PRECIPITATION. As with temperatures, there are great and often sharp differences in precipitation in mountainous regions.

Slopes which lie in the path of moisture-bearing winds have heavy rain or snowfall while a few miles away, on leeward slopes, there may be very little. Where there is a change in wind direction, such as at Darjeeling where monsoonal winds strike the lower slopes of the Himalayas in summer, there are great seasonal contrasts in the amount of precipitation. The heavy precipitation on windward sides of mountains is, of course, orographic in nature. In mountainous areas that are surrounded by rainy tropical or arid climates, precipitation, or the lack of it, results from the same climatic controls which affect the adjacent areas.

RELATED ENVIRONMENTAL FEATURES. Differences in vegetation cover, which result from variation in temperature or precipitation, are a very significant aspect of the natural environment of mountains. Steep slopes and narrow valleys preclude the development of unique types of soil and there are few meaningful generalizations that can be made about the native animal life.

The temperature changes which occur in mountains are reflected in the noticeable vertical zonation of natural vegetation. The altitudinal belts of climate and vegetation are so well defined in the tropics and subtropics of Latin America that they have been given distinctive names. A lower zone, *tierra caliente,* of high temperatures and heavy rainfall which extends up to 2,000 or 3,000 feet has the dense forest vegetation of the rainy tropical climates. Above this, up to 5,500 or 6,000 feet, lies the *tierra templada* or a zone of moderate temperatures, with a mixed forest of evergreen and deciduous broadleaf trees. In the next higher belt, called the *tierra fria,* which extends to 10,000 or 11,500 feet, the broadleaf forests give way to coniferous trees. The upper limit of the tierra fria corresponds to the treeline, beyond which is a zone of mountain meadows that finally is succeeded, at altitudes of 14,000 to 15,000 feet, by permanent snow and ice.

The altitudinal limits of the vegetation zones vary considerably with latitude and amount of precipitation. On leeward slopes where the precipitation is very light, the vertical zones may not be evident and the vegetation may be limited to either scrub forest or desert scrub. Outside of Latin America the vertical climate zones or bands may not be distinguished by name, but the zones generally are typical of all mountain regions. In the middle and high latitudes there are fewer and less conspicuous zones because the tierra caliente and often the tierra templada are missing. Where there are many farmers in mountainous regions, there is a corresponding zonation of crops and agricultural activity.

SUPPLEMENTARY READING

Blair, Thomas A. *Climatology.* New York: Prentice-Hall, Inc., 1942.

Brooks, Charles E. P. *Climate Through the Ages.* New York: McGraw-Hill Book Co., Inc., 1949.

Climate and Man. The Yearbook of Agriculture, 1941, U.S. Department of Agriculture. Washington, D.C.: Government Printing Office, 1941.

Critchfield, H. J. *General Climatology.* Englewood Cliffs, N.J.: Prentice-Hall, Inc., 1966.

Haurwitz, Bernhard, and Austin, James M. *Climatology.* New York: McGraw-Hill Book Co., Inc., 1944.

Kendrew, Wilfred G. *Climates of the Continents.* 5th ed. New York: Oxford University Press, 1961.

Kendrew, Wilfred G. *Climatology.* 2nd ed. New York: Oxford University Press, 1957.

Koeppe, Clarence E., and DeLong, G. C. *Weather and Climate.* New York: McGraw-Hill Book Co., Inc., 1958.

Trewartha, Glenn T. *An Introduction to Climate.* 3rd ed. New York: McGraw-Hill Book Co., Inc., 1954.

Trewartha, Glenn T. *The Earth's Problem Climates.* Madison: University of Wisconsin Press, 1961.

5

The Origins of Surface Features

The exposed portion of the earth's crust differs greatly from one place to another in elevation, slope, material, and arrangement. At any place the shape and features of the terrain are the result of many centuries of interaction between forces within the earth which act to cause differences in elevation and other forces from without which act to eliminate these differences. The rapidity at which change occurs in an area, and the resulting modifications in surface features, are related to the nature of the earth materials and are greatly affected by climatic conditions.

EARTH MATERIALS

Planet earth is an almost spherical body with a radius of approximately 4,000 miles. It is believed that the internal structure of the earth consists of an inner core, a surrounding mantle, and an outer shell or crust. Geophysicists tell us that the interior core of the earth, which extends from the center outward approximately 2,150 miles, is composed of iron and nickel. The outer portion of the very dense material which makes up this core is in a molten state but the inner part, to a radius of about 750 miles, is probably solid. The mantle, which extends about 1,800 miles outward from the core, is made up of material generally of great rigidity and high density. However, it is believed that the portion of the mantle which lies immediately adjacent to the crust has conditions of temperature and pressure which cause it to be subject to slow flowage over long periods of time, and the crust of the earth more or less floats upon this viscous outer portion of the mantle. The outer shell or crust of the earth is a layer of rocks of low density, and varies in thickness from 10 to 40 miles; the thicker portion is over the continents and the thinner portion under the

84

ocean floor. The rocks which make up the outer shell of the earth are composed of varying combinations of chemical elements or minerals.

Chemical Elements of the Earth's Crust. Although 92 chemical elements are known to be found in the earth's crust, most of them do not occur in great quantity or in a pure state. Only four are really abundant (oxygen 46.6 per cent, silicon 27.7 per cent, aluminum 8.1 per cent, and iron 5 per cent) and together they constitute 87 per cent of the entire mass. Calcium, sodium, potassium, and magnesium make up another 11.1 per cent of the total. None of the remaining elements accounts for more than 0.5 per cent and most are present only in trace amounts. The eight elements which make up approximately 98 per cent of the earth's crust are the most important ingredients of minerals.

Minerals. Most minerals are combinations of two or more elements which occur in chemical union, but there are a few, such as pure copper and gold, which are composed of a single chemical element. Minerals are natural inorganic substances with fairly definite chemical compositions and with distinctive physical characteristics such as crystal form, hardness, color, luster, and manner of fracture. There are hundreds of minerals but, as in the case of elements, a relatively small number make up the bulk of the earth's solid material. The minerals present and the way in which they are combined determine the type and characteristics of rocks.

Rocks. Rocks are generally defined as aggregates of minerals. Although a few rocks are made up primarily of one mineral, most of them are mixtures of two or more. The minerals which make up a particular type of rock appear as separate particles, not in chemical combination or in identical amounts. The most common method of classifying rocks is to group them according to their origins:

1. *Igneous rocks* are those which have resulted from the solidification of molten matter. Some were formed by the cooling of lava that was forced from the interior of the earth out into the atmosphere; others represent the solidification of fluid material far underground. Where the cooling took place slowly below the surface the rock is coarse grained, as is the case of many granites. When the molten material is exposed to the open air and solidification is rapid a fine-grained rock results, such as basalt. Granites,

which are probably the most common of the igneous rocks, contain large amounts of quartz and feldspar, together with some dark ferro-magnesium substances. Basalt, which is another widespread variety, is composed largely of ferro-magnesium minerals. Other common igneous rocks are syenite, rhyolite, gabbro, and obsidian.

2. *Sedimentary rocks* are made up of particles of solid matter that have been deposited in horizontal layers and later consolidated into rock. They represent accumulations of the broken-up particles of other rocks or minerals that have been transported by running water, wind, or glaciers. Most of the sedimentary rocks were formed in the bottoms of lakes or shallow seas. Sandstone is made up of grains of sand, limestone is derived from the skeletal remains of sea organisms or calcium carbonate precipitated in sea water, and conglomerate is composed of gravel. Fine particles of silt, clay, or mud may be transformed into a rock called shale. Because the sediments from which these rocks are formed accumulate over long periods of time, interruptions in the process and variations in the material being deposited give them a distinctly layered or stratified appearance.

3. *Metamorphic rocks* are those which are the result of marked alteration in previously existing rocks and minerals. The change may be the result of pressures which accompany earth movement, the presence of heat which accompanies the movement of molten material, or the chemical action of underground water. When such conditions occur sandstone slowly becomes quartzite, shale changes into slate, limestone becomes marble, granite forms a coarsely banded rock called gneiss, and basalt turns into a finely streaked schist. Of course, the processes which form metamorphic rocks take place over long periods of time.

INTERNAL FORCES AFFECTING SURFACE FEATURES

Many of the causes of differences in surface features originate from within the earth's interior and are usually termed the *tectonic forces*. Their energy results from expansion, contraction, or the transfer of molten matter and causes the building up of features of great height in some places and the formation of widespread depressions in others. The tectonic forces involve both the deformation of the earth's crust itself (diastrophism) and the movement of molten material from one place to another (vulcanism).

Diastrophism. The several forms of diastrophism include rock folding, uplifting, downwarping, earth movement, and other actions which cause portions of the earth's crust to be elevated or depressed.

Folding or bending occurs when rock layers are subjected to great stress and strain. Horizontal compression can result in the formation of one or more arches or upfolds called *anticlines,* separated by troughs or downfolds called *synclines* (see Fig. 24). Folding may form a simple arch limited to a small area or may take place over several hundred square miles and result in the

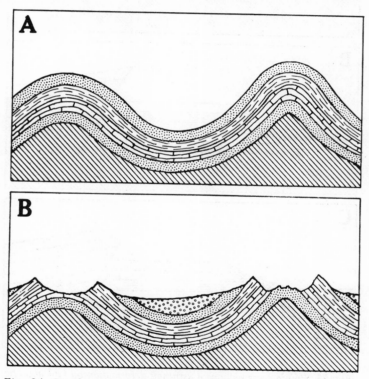

Fig. 24. Simple cross sections illustrating deformation by folding. Diagram A shows uneroded folds. Diagram B shows surface forms which result from the erosion of softer rocks, leaving the more resistant layers standing out as ridges.

development of ridges and valleys of very large proportions. In regions where folding has occurred the rock structures may also have become fractured. Since folding usually involves long periods of time, there are few places on earth where the ridges

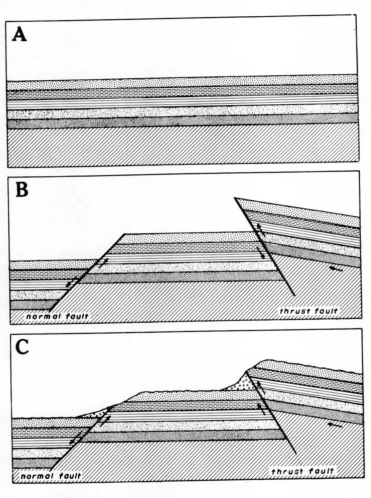

Fig. 25. *Simple cross sections illustrating deformation by faulting. Diagram A shows undisturbed layers of sedimentary rock. Diagram B shows two faults as they might appear if there is no erosion; displacement is vertical. Diagram C indicates how faulted areas appear after being eroded.*

represent the original anticlines and the valleys the synclines because the forces of weathering and erosion, which are accelerated at higher elevations, have altered the appearance of the terrain. However, generally the ridges represent the more resistant tilted rock layers and the valleys the softer materials which have been broken up and carried away.

Warping is a less intense type of deformation than folding and takes place when broad areas of the earth are slowly lowered or elevated over long periods of time. In some instances wide expanses of land around the shores of seas or ocean basins have been gradually covered by water; in others, large areas once a part of the ocean floor have been elevated and have become part of the land surface of the world.

Faulting occurs when pressures in the earth's crust are strong enough to cause fracture and displacement. Such a break in rock structure along which there has been movement is called a *fault*. In some faults the movement is vertical, causing one side to be pushed above the other; in others the displacement is horizontal, resulting in an offset of existing natural and man-made features (see Fig. 25). Like folding, faulting may occur in a limited space and result in minor changes at the surface or it may cause the widespread deformation of broad areas. *Earthquakes* are movements of the earth's crust which may be sensed or measured at the surface. They usually occur along fault lines and may or may not be accompanied by visible change.

Vulcanism. All movement of igneous or molten matter, whether it reaches the outer portion of the earth's crust or not, is called vulcanism. The transfer of material in this state is frequently accompanied, preceded, or followed by earth movement. The masses of molten matter cool or harden and become igneous rock.

Extrusive vulcanism takes place when *lava*, which is molten rock, reaches the surface before becoming solidified. The lava may flow quietly from fractures in the outer crust and quickly solidify or it may harden slowly and spread out in horizontal sheets over a wide area. Some igneous extrusions are explosive in the sense that cinders, ash, and rock fragments may be violently blown from the craters of volcanoes or from vents at the earth's surface.

The most spectacular form of extrusive vulcanism is the cone-shaped volcanic mountain (see Fig. 26). Peaks of this type are built up of rock fragments, cinders, ash, dust, and other forms of cooled lava. They are steep-sided when formed from explosive volcanic eruptions or from accumulations of lavas which solidify quickly. Lavas which congeal slowly produce peaks that cover larger areas and have more gentle slopes. Some lavas are so highly viscous and slow cooling that they flow out from cracks in the earth's crust and cover hundreds of square miles in horizontal layers obliterating the pre-existing surface.

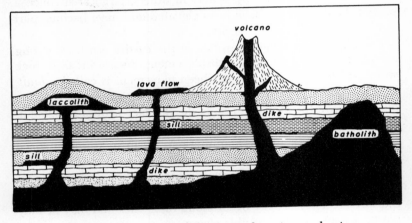

Fig. 26. *Diagram showing forms resulting from vulcanism.*

Intrusive vulcanism involves molten material that moves through the rocks of the earth's outer shell and hardens before it reaches the atmosphere. This intrusive molten material, which is called *magma*, may work vertically through fractures in underground structures or force itself between horizontal rock layers. Igneous intrusions may be accompanied or followed by diastrophism and hundreds of years after cooling may become exposed on the surface by erosion.

A quantity of magma which has become solidified in a vertical fracture is known as a *dike;* when it works in between layers of stratified rocks and hardens, the horizontal sheets which it forms are called *sills.* Huge masses of igneous matter which have pushed outward from the interior of the earth and form the core of many great mountain systems are known as *batholiths*. When magma flows between layers of sedimentary rocks near the surface and causes the overlying strata to be pushed upward, the intrusive mass is called a *laccolith*. Laccoliths, batholiths, dikes, and sills are made up of materials that solidified below the surface and are generally harder than the rocks which surround them. After long periods of erosion they may become exposed and stand out as hills, mountains, or other prominent features on the landscape.

EXTERNAL FORCES AFFECTING SURFACE FEATURES

Whenever portions of the earth's surface are being uplifted by diastrophism or vulcanism, they are simultaneously under attack by a number of forces which work to reduce elevation. These processes, which have the effect of wearing down heights of land and filling in low places, originate outside the earth's crust and are greatly influenced by atmospheric conditions. One group of these forces, collectively called *weathering*, breaks solid rocks into particles that are small enough to be moved and transported elsewhere. The processes by which these fragments of earth material are picked up, removed, and deposited in another place are referred to as the agents of *erosion*. It is not always possible to determine where weathering stops and erosion begins, they are so closely related, but there is probably no portion of the earth's surface which has not been affected by both. In some areas weathering has resulted in accumulations of broken rock materials that cover unaltered bedrock.

Weathering. The methods by which solid rock is prepared for removal may be either chemical or mechanical in nature. Neither involves any significant movement of material.

Chemical weathering occurs when rock substances are decomposed and a chemical change takes place. Oxygen, carbon dioxide, or water may dissolve certain elements from some rock minerals and form a chemical union with others. The most important chemical processes are oxidation, carbonation, hydration, and solution. They participate in breaking up solid materials by forming new minerals which are softer or more soluble than the old, or by dissolving minerals and carrying them away, or by causing fractures with the expansion which accompanies some chemical changes. Since all these processes require the presence of water, and since chemical decomposition is encouraged by high temperatures, chemical weathering is most active in warm humid climates.

Mechanical weathering involves those methods by which rocks are physically fragmented, or disintegrated, without chemical change. During the processes of cooling which form igneous rocks (and the compaction which results in the formation of sedimentary rocks), cracks and crevices may develop in the rock structure. These cracks may be enlarged by the expansion of water freezing in the crevices, by the prying action of plant roots, or even by the burrowing of animals. Rapid heating and cooling of rock structures, as occurs in desert regions, is another important process of disintegration. Any scraping, grinding, abrasive, or jarring action that takes place when fragments are being transported by water, ice, or wind results in mechanical weathering. Mechanical weathering is most active under conditions which do not encourage chemical decomposition, particularly in those areas with cold or dry climates.

Erosion and Deposition. The weathered material that has accumulated on the surface of the earth is known as *mantle rock* or *regolith*, and the removal of this material is called *erosion*. The most important agents of erosion are running water, moving ice, and winds. Less widespread in their erosive effects but nevertheless important in limited areas are the motions of ocean waters and the action of underground water, and some particles of material are transported short distances by gravity. The laying down of the material in a new location is known as *deposition*.

Effect of Running Water. Running water is probably the most important of the forces which, through transportation and deposition of matter, have influenced the nature of the world's landforms. It is obviously most effective in regions with humid climates, but even in dry areas the surface features of the land derive many characteristics from the action of moving water.

The rate at which running water wears away the earth's surface is influenced by a number of conditions, but chiefly by the volume of water present and the speed at which it moves. The amount of water is a reflection of the nature of the precipitation, and the velocity results from the slope of the land. When rainfall occurs on slopes, or whenever snow and ice begin to melt, water forms into rivulets and streams which quickly develop the capacity to pick up unattached materials. Erosion is most effective under conditions of heavy precipitation, and the steeper the gradient, the larger the particles and the greater the quantity of material that will be picked up and transported elsewhere. Running water moves dislodged particles by rolling them along the surface, by lifting them and bouncing them short distances down slopes, or by picking them up and carrying them along in suspension. The amount of wearing away that takes place depends also upon the quantity and nature of the material being transported and the type of surface over which the water is flowing. The load may have an abrasive action upon the underlying surface and the cutting power will be greater on soft or loosely consolidated rocks than on hard or tightly cemented structures.

Running water deposits all or part of its load at places where its velocity decreases, where there is a loss of volume through evaporation or seepage, or where there is a marked increase in the amount of material added to the flow. The accumulations of earth material laid down in water are called *alluvium,* and the deposition of alluvium takes a number of forms. Broad expanses of land in stream valleys have been built up by the overflow of water during or following periods of excessive runoff. Such deposits, known as *flood plains,* accumulate when the speed of the overflow decreases. In many cases the deposits of material are thickest near the stream itself, causing the surface water in normal times to be actually higher than the land at the margins of the valley. The higher lands near streams which deposit alluvium in this manner are called *natural levees.*

The gradient of many streams is marked by one or more places where there is a sharp decrease in slope and an accompanying decline in the velocity of the water. In such places, as at the foot of hills or mountains, streams will drop part of the material they are carrying and form what are known as *alluvial fans* (see Fig. 27). These accumulations, which are particularly conspicuous in areas of low and infrequent rainfall, resemble segments of broad shallow cones with the highest and narrowest portions being located near the point where the change in gradient occurs. The deposition of large quantities of alluvium clogs the stream and causes it

DELTA.

ALLUVIAL FANS.

Fig. 27. Features formed by stream deposition.

to shift its course or spread out into a number of small channels, each of which deposits some of the burden. As the speed of flow diminishes the size of the particles that can be carried decreases; therefore an important characteristic of alluvial fans is that the particles of which they are made become increasingly smaller toward the outer margins of the fans.

Where flowing streams empty into the relatively quiet waters of lakes, seas, and oceans they often construct features known as *deltas* (see Fig. 27). Like alluvial fans, deltas are frequently triangular in shape and tend to have coarser materials near the point where deposition begins to occur. When deltas are formed, the accumulation of alluvium may cause the water course to become choked with sand or mud and a number of secondary or distributary channels may develop. For this reason, many rivers which have formed deltas separate into several mouths as they enter the sea.

EFFECT OF MOVING ICE. *Glaciers* are accumulations of ice which have become so large that sufficient pressure is created to cause movement along the outer margins of the mass. They are formed when more snow falls on an area during cold seasons than melts during the warm months; a residue of snow remains and is added to each year. If this condition exists for a number of years, the snow near the bottom of the mass becomes transformed into ice, and if the weight of the mass is sufficiently heavy, the ice will slowly move away from the center of pressure.

Glaciers are found in the upper elevations of some mountainous regions and on land areas in the high latitudes. *Mountain or valley glaciers* occur where the snow and ice accumulation results from high altitude; many of the crests of the great mountain systems of the world are marked by glaciers which move not only because of the weight of the mass of ice but also because of the force of gravity which causes them to move down the adjacent valleys. *Continental glaciers* occur where the accumulation is caused by high latitude and are found only on Greenland and Antarctica. In past geologic times, large parts of North America, Eurasia, and other land masses were covered with ice sheets; these have disappeared but nevertheless they have given the areas distinctive surface features.

The glacial erosion of the land commences when the glacial ice becomes frozen to the material upon which it rests. As the mass begins to move it plucks up pieces of this material and carries them along. The fragments that are transported by glaciers are circulated within the ice mass and are ground together, their sharp edges are worn away, and their size is reduced. As the ice and the material being carried moves along, an abrasive action is exerted upon the underlying land surface which tends to wear it down and to remove its irregularities. Glaciers will continue to advance so long as the outward movement is greater than the melting of the ice around the margins. As mountain glaciers extend down valleys they eventually encounter higher temperatures and the ice begins to melt away. This also happens when continental glaciers advance into lower latitude zones with higher temperatures. The meltwaters of glacial ice form into streams which behave much like those formed by direct precipitation.

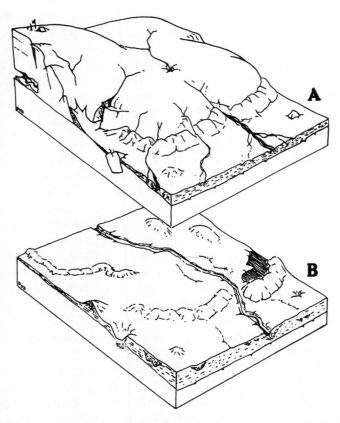

Fig. 28. Features resulting from deposition by a continental glacier. Diagram A shows a plain partly covered by glacial ice. Diagram B is the same plain after the ice has melted. Note the moraine which formed around the margin of the ice sheet. Other features shown include a ground moraine, an esker, kames, kettle holes, and part of an outwash plain. (DRAWING BY PETER VAN DUSEN.)

In an earlier time the continental glaciers advanced equatorward over northern hemisphere continents and altered the existing landscape by erosive action near their places of origin and by deposition near their margins. Vast areas of Canada, Scandinavia, and Siberia were scoured by glacial action, which left a surface with lower relief and many broad areas devoid of mantle rock. Often these areas were marked by parallel grooves or *striations,* which indicated the direction of the glacial movement. The regions affected by glacial erosion usually had their higher elevations worn down and many low places filled with glacial debris. Where the underlying rocks were soft or loosely consolidated, large basins were scooped out and these became filled with water as the ice receded. In other places glacial movement ceased for a period of years and material was deposited which dammed existing valleys. Regions affected by glacial scour are characterized by irregular drainage patterns and the presence of numerous lakes.

As the continental glaciers progressed equatorward from their places of origin, the material they deposited, known as *glacial drift,* formed irregular groups of hills, ridges, and depressions called *moraines* (see Fig. 28). Those deposits which mark the farthest advance of the ice front are called *terminal moraines;* those laid down during the advance or retreat of the ice are *recessional moraines;* and the areas of gently rolling landscape lacking conspicuous features, which are the deposits laid down under the ice between other moraines, are termed *ground moraines.* Areas behind terminal and recessional moraines frequently are dotted with low half-egg-shaped hills made up of clayey material that was deposited beneath glacial ice. These *drumlins* are elongated in the direction of ice movement; the long gentle slope of each drumlin points toward the moraine and the steep end faces the source of the glacier. There also are numerous minor surface features associated with deposition by continental glaciers: low winding ridges called *eskers* represent drainage ways within the ice mass which became blocked and caused the material being carried to be deposited; *kames* are low irregular hills of stratified drift which were formed under glacial ice; and *kettle holes* are depressions marking the places where large chunks of ice were buried under glacial debris and later melted. Areas in front of melting glaciers received large amounts of earth

Fig. 29. Glaciated mountains. Note the arete and the horns in the background, two cirques at center-left, and the hanging valley in the foreground.

materials which were carried beyond the ice front by the running water and were deposited as *outwash plains*. The melting ice created vast quantities of water which widened the valleys of existing drainage courses and in some areas formed large lakes. When the ice retreated, the broad valleys which had been formed accommodated only insignificant streams and the larger lakes contracted, leaving broad areas of flat *glacio-lacustrine plains* around their margins.

Many of the features formed by mountain or valley glaciers are similar to those resulting from the continental type, but some are unique. Highland regions with mountain glaciers have *cirques,* or basins partially surrounded by steep headwalls, which were excavated by the plucking of glacial ice; *aretes* are high, narrow, and jagged ridges which represent the separation between two cirques; and lofty narrow peaks, called *horns,* are located where three or more cirques encroached upon each other. (See Fig. 29.) As the ice pushes down valleys its erosive action is exerted sideward as well as downward and gouges out troughs with broad flat floors and almost vertical sides. Tributary streams or glaciers join these valleys on top of the ice, giving them little gradient and (after the ice has disappeared) leaving numerous *hanging valleys* many of which are today occupied by spectacular waterfalls. As a mountain or valley glacier advances downslope it may, like continental types, form lakes either by gouging out softer rocks or by damming existing drainage. It also will form moraines and glacio-fluvial features near its outer margins.

WIND EROSION. Compared to erosion by running water and glacial ice, wind erosion is relatively unimportant in the moulding of surface features. However, wind may move dust, sand, or even gravel in sufficient quantities to cause changes in terrain that are of local significance. The most noticeable results of wind action are found in dry climates, but this agent of erosion may also remove fine materials from the shores of lakes, dry flood plains, and heavily cultivated areas in humid regions.

The process by which wind erodes the surface materials of one place and transports them to another is called *deflation*. This action is similar to that of running water; particles may be rolled, slid, bounced, and at times even picked up and carried considerable distance. Like streams, winds transport larger quantities and larger particles when they are moving at greater velocities. Wind erosion may result in depressions, or *blowouts*, in areas that have been deflated, but more commonly the result is the removal of finer materials leaving a gravelly desert surface known as *reg*. Winds which are carrying earth materials may have a sandblasting effect upon exposed boulders and cliffs by wearing away the softer rocks and leaving the harder portions undisturbed.

Dusts and sands accumulate on the leeward sides of areas which are susceptible to wind erosion. Usually sand is not carried great distances. *Dunes*, which are accumulations of windblown sand, are common in desert regions and on the margins of deserts. In general, sand dunes have gentle slopes facing the direction from which the wind is blowing and steep slopes on their leeward sides, and they are most prominent where bushes or boulders act as obstacles around which the blowing sand can accumulate. The most spectacular form of sand dune is the *barchan*, a crescent-shaped dune with its two points facing with the prevailing wind direction. Broad areas with undulating deposits of sand are called *erg.* In humid regions, strong winds may rework sand found along the shores of large lakes and form dunes of considerable size.

The fine materials of temporarily dry river plains, glacial deposits, over-cropped farms, and deserts may be transported considerable distance and laid down as *loess.* Deposits of windblown dust are frequently found in humid climates, and where uneroded they may form the parent material of very productive agricultural soils.

SUBSURFACE WATER.   Under some conditions, subsurface water may be an important element in the shaping of surface features. Water from rain or melting snow which sinks below the surface, at times to great depths, is known as *ground water.* It may percolate downward in such quantities that it completely fills the openings between individual soil and rock particles. The top of this saturated zone is referred to as the *water table.*

In certain types of rock, particularly limestone, water seeping through subsurface layers will dissolve and remove soluble minerals. If the process continues, cracks and openings in the rock will become enlarged and caves will be formed. Water dripping into caves and caverns located above the water table frequently evaporates and deposits calcium minerals on the ceiling in icicle-like shapes called *stalactites.* Drippings from the roofs of caves build up accumulations on the floors which are known as *stalagmites.*

Where the break-up of rocks by solution is active, the drainage of water from precipitation on the surface may be mainly underground. Water seeps down through upper layers and drains away through subterranean channels. Not infrequently the terrain of regions with this type of drainage will have numerous depressions, or *sink holes,* which represent places where the roofs of caves have collapsed. Areas with few streams, and having underground drainage, sink holes, and caves, form a unique type of land surface known as *karst.*

EFFECT OF OCEAN WAVES AND CURRENTS.   Ocean waves and currents are constantly at work modifying the coastal areas of continents and islands, either by erosion or deposition. Waves, which are caused by the wind, may smash or roll against the shore and gradually wear away the land. Erosive action takes place both above and below the average water level, in the zone between the crests of waves at high tide and the troughs separating waves at low tide. As waves cut into the land on bold coasts they produce steep *wave-cut cliffs* above the water level and *wave-cut terraces* below the water level. The materials which are removed from the land are often deposited just beyond the wave-cut terraces in the form of *wave-built terraces*. Where the coastline is low and the water offshore is shallow, deposition becomes more prominent than removal. Waves entering shallow waters drag the bottom and pick up loose fragments which are dropped as the waves break and topple over. This action builds up low strips of land called *offshore bars* which parallel the coastline and are separated from it by shallow lagoons. Offshore bars attached to the coast at the entrances to bays or other indentations are termed *spits;* curved spits are called *hooks.* Spits and hooks are most prominent where there are currents of ocean water moving parallel to the coast.

SUPPLEMENTARY READING

Bradley, John H. *Autobiography of Earth.* New York: Coward-McCann, Inc., 1935.

Cotton, C. A. *Landscape, as Developed by the Processes of Normal Erosion.* 2nd ed. New York: John Wiley & Sons, Inc., 1948.

Croneis, Carey, and Krumbein, William C. *Down to Earth.* Chicago: University of Chicago Press, 1936.

Davis, William M. *Geographical Essays.* New York: Dover Publications, Inc., 1954. (Originally published in 1909 by Ginn & Co., Boston.)

Gamow, George. *Biography of the Earth.* New York: Viking Press, 1948.

Leet, L. D., and Judson, Sheldon. *Physical Geology.* 3rd ed. Englewood Cliffs, N.J.: Prentice-Hall, Inc., 1965.

Lobeck, A. K. *Geomorphology.* New York: McGraw-Hill Book Co., Inc., 1939.

Longwell, Chester R.; Knopf, Adolph; and Flint, Richard F. *Outlines of Physical Geology.* 2nd ed. New York: John Wiley & Sons, Inc., 1941.

Putnam, William C. *Geology*. New York: Oxford University Press, 1964.

Thornbury, W. D. *Principles of Geomorphology*. New York: John Wiley & Sons, Inc., 1954.

6

Major Types of Landforms

Over the centuries, the internal and external forces which have shaped the earth's crust have varied so greatly and have occurred under such diverse climatic conditions that no two places on earth are exactly alike in their surface features or landforms. However, it is possible to recognize a relatively small number of terrain types which have many features in common. Such a classification enables geographers to compare and contrast the terrain of general areas without describing the specific details of individual features. It also gives definite values to terms which in common usage are subject to considerable variation: for example, what is a mountain to a native of Kansas might be considered a small hill by a resident of western Colorado, and the term "plateau" may have entirely different meanings for residents of North Carolina and those living in Arizona.

The landform classification commonly utilized by geographers is based upon differences and similarities resulting from variation in local relief and in the amount of land in slope. (See Fig. 30.) The term "local relief" applies to the difference in elevation between the top of the highest ridge and the bottom of the lowest valley in a restricted area. Its connotation is quite different from that of altitude or elevation above sea level. Mountains and hills have most of their land in slope and moderate to high relief; plains and plateaus have surfaces that are predominantly level or gently sloping and low relief. These four major types of landforms may be defined as follows:

Mountains have most of their surface in slope and reach comparatively high altitudes. Local relief is in excess of 2,000 feet, a figure which usually indicates that there are differences in elevation sufficiently great to cause variation in natural vegetation and climate. This variation is characteristic of mountains but not of hills.

Hills have predominantly sloping land and are usually found at intermediate elevations. Local relief is more than 500 feet and less than 2,000 feet. Usually slopes are not as steep nor are elevations as high as in mountains.

Plains are areas of low relief and low altitude. Local relief is less than 500 feet and elevations are usually, but not always, less than 2,000 feet above sea level.

Plateaus, sometimes called *tablelands,* are areas of relatively level land which have some places with high relief. They are usually more than 2,000 feet above sea level and include some valleys and/or ridges with local relief in excess of 500 feet. Most plateaus have steep slopes or escarpments on one or more of their margins.

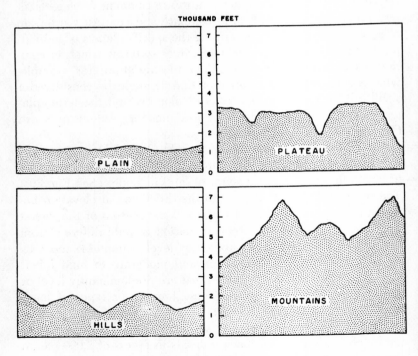

Fig. 30. Diagram illustrating the relief and elevation characteristics of the four major types of landforms.

There is great diversity in the surface features of each of the four major types of landforms, and differences within each type result from the varied conditions which caused the formation of the original surfaces, the weathering and erosion that have been present, and variations in slope and local relief.

Fig. 31. Diagram of eroded faulted and folded mountains in southern New Guinea. (ADAPTED FROM COMMONWEALTH SCIENTIFIC AND INDUSTRIAL RESEARCH ORGANIZATION, AUSTRALIA, REPORT.)

MOUNTAINS

Although undoubtedly the most spectacular of all landform types, mountains are also the most inhospitable to human beings. Their rugged surfaces make movement and the development of means of transportation difficult; their steep slopes, accompanied by the lower temperatures associated with increased elevation, are unfavorable for agriculture. Because of these obstacles few broad mountainous areas are densely populated and many are practically uninhabited.

Characteristics of Mountains. For man, the most important features of mountains are the large amount of land in steep slopes and the small extent of areas of low relief (see Fig. 31). Mountains differ from hills in that they have greater local relief, higher elevations, altitudinal differences in climate, and a more massive appearance. Although some mountains do have almost perpendicular cliffs, only a few places have gradients exceeding 65 degrees or even 40 degrees from horizontal, and the average slope in most mountainous regions is in the neighborhood of 25 degrees from horizontal. Successive areas with relatively gentle slope separated by sharp rises are more common than sheer vertical ascents.

Some mountains are broad and have rounded summits, others are made up of numerous jagged peaks, and some consist of several narrow ridges. A few peaks in the great highland region of south central Asia approach 30,000 feet in elevation but in other parts of the world the greatest heights lie between 17,000 and 23,000 feet above sea level. Peaks with elevations in excess of 17,000 feet usually do not rise from sea level in one continuous slope, but are perched on top of broad upland masses which have average elevations between 5,000 and 10,000 feet. In comparison, some of the most notable individual mountains are those which rise to modest heights from plains or coastal regions.

The appearance of mountainous areas is determined by the nature of the rocks of which they are composed, the tectonic forces which brought them into being, and the erosive agents which have acted upon them. Most classifications of mountains are based upon the processes that caused the land to be elevated but descriptions often include terms which refer to the extent to which the surfaces have been altered by weathering and erosion. *Young* or *youthful mountains* are those which have recently been uplifted or are still in the process of being formed. They tend to be of high elevation, are rugged in appearance, and bear prominent evidence of the tectonic activity that caused them to be built up. *Mature mountains* are more stable and erosive action has obscured some of the original features. Running water has deepened valleys in some places and has deposited material in others, and erosive forces have worked upon the slopes, widening valleys and reducing the elevation of summits. *Old mountains* are those which have remained undisturbed for long periods of time and have undergone excessive weathering and erosion. Elevations have been greatly lowered, ridge crests tend to be broad and rounded, valleys are wide and shallow. The appearance of mountain regions also varies with the nature of the erosive forces that have sculptured their surfaces. Stream-eroded highlands differ greatly from those which have been affected by mountain glaciers.

Types of Mountains. Each one of the many types of mountains represents an area where tectonic forces have been more active in uplifting land surfaces than external processes have been in wearing them down.

1. *Faulted mountains* occur (*a*) where diastrophism has caused

the land on one side of a fracture in the earth's crust to be pushed upward and tilted—these are termed *block fault mountains;* or (*b*) where the surface on one side of the break has become lowered with reference to the other, in a *normal fault.* Although block fault mountains are more spectacular, both types usually have ridges with one steep slope and one that is gentle. In several parts of the world more or less parallel faults have occurred, causing the land lying between the fractures to subside and leaving a broad *rift valley* bordered by escarpments. The downfaulted area may also be known as a *graben* and the uplifted sides as *horsts.*

2. *Folded mountains* are formed where horizontal compression upon surface layers has caused bending and buckling to be more prominent than fracture. In some cases pressures have been sufficient to cause sedimentary layers to be jammed together and pushed into a series of ridges and valleys. Since rock layers vary greatly in resistance to erosion and erosive processes evolve slowly over long periods of time, the ridges in most folded mountains represent the layers made up of harder materials and the valleys typify the softer rocks. The Appalachian ridge and valley country of the eastern United States was formed in this manner.

3. *Domed mountains* result when *laccoliths,* or intrusions of igneous rocks between sedimentary layers, cause the overlying surface to become elevated. When such conditions occur, strata surrounding the uplifted area are subject to greater weathering and erosion. In time, the higher portions are worn away, leaving the igneous material exposed and surrounded by a series of inclined ridges with steep slopes facing inward. These ridges which represent differential erosion of hard and soft layers are called *cuestas;* they may also be found in broad areas of sedimentary rocks that have experienced minor faults.

4. *Volcanic mountains* result from accumulations of extrusive igneous materials. Steep-sided volcanic cones are built up by lavas which solidify rapidly and by the accumulated debris of explosive eruptions. The tops of some former volcanoes have been removed, either by explosion or by collapse of the apex, leaving huge pits or basins at the summit. These *craters* or *calderas* may appear as upland plains surrounded by cliffs or, as in the case of Crater Lake in Oregon, may be partially filled with water. When molten rock materials cool slowly, the resulting

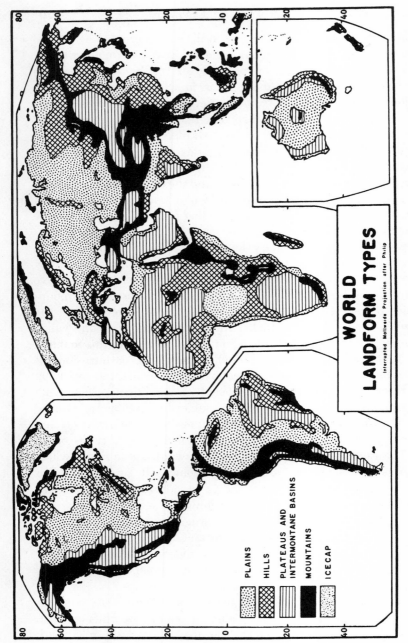

WORLD LANDFORM TYPES

Interrupted Mollweide Projection after Philip

PLAINS
HILLS
PLATEAUS AND INTERMONTANE BASINS
MOUNTAINS
ICECAP

Fig. 32.

peaks have broader summit areas and slopes that are less steep. Mountains of this type, such as Mauna Loa in Hawaii, are termed *shield* or *dome volcanoes.*

It should be noted that there are few upland areas of the world which were formed by a single process and that most highland regions were built up by several mountain-forming processes. When molten material moves from one place to another within or upon the earth's crust there is a readjustment within the rock structures which may cause earthquakes and faulting to take place. On the other hand, the fracturing which accompanies faulting may be sufficient to permit molten matter to begin to flow. Folding and faulting are often closely associated with each other in mountain formation.

The Distribution of Mountains. Most of the great mountain belts of the world are arranged as four branches fanning outward from a vast upland area located in south central Asia (see Fig. 32). From this node of convergence the Tien Shan, Altai, Yablonoi, and other ranges extend northeastward to the Bering Strait. Just eastward, in North America, the Alaskan ranges extend southward to the western coastal mountains and the Rocky Mountain system of Canada and the United States. These north-south highlands continue into Mexico to approximately 20 degrees of latitude, where they veer to the southeast through Central America to join the Andes of South America. The Andes continue in an unbroken chain some 4,500 miles to the southern end of the continent. A second great mountain branch reaches east through the Kunlun and Himalayan ranges, then south through the narrow ranges of southeastern Asia, and reappears in the highland regions of the East Indies. The mountains of New Zealand and eastern Australia represent subsidiary branches of this system. The third major offshoot runs west through southwestern Asia; crosses southern Europe via the Carpathians, Alps, and Pyrenees; and breaks off in the Atlas Mountains of northwestern Africa. The fourth branch is a discontinuous group of highlands extending from the borders of the Red Sea through Ethiopia and the African lakes district to the southern portion of the African continent. The individual ranges in the branches which extend out from south central Asia generally are high, rugged, and youthful in appearance. Associated with them are numerous hilly regions, tablelands, and intermontane basins.

Mountainous regions of the world located outside of the four principal branches tend to be more scattered in their distribution and lower in elevation. Such areas are found in Japan and Korea, in the Urals Range of the Soviet Union, and in the West Indies.

The Appalachian system of the eastern United States, the Brazilian and Guiana highlands of South America, and many of the upland areas of Africa contain the remnants of older, once higher, surfaces that have long been subjected to weathering and erosion. They tend to have broader summit areas, wider valleys, lower elevations, and less conspicuous vertical zonation than the mountain systems previously described.

Man's Utilization of Mountains. The hardships that mountains impose upon human settlement explain why highland regions are inhabited by not more than 12 per cent of the world's population. The steep slopes make cultivation of the land difficult and hinder attempts to control soil erosion. In areas where the population density is high, cultivation may extend up slopes of considerable grade, or terraces may be constructed, but most of the farming in mountains is concentrated upon the small patches of level land that may be found in basins or valleys. Since temperatures become lower with increases in elevation, farming in highland regions is in some cases restricted, and in others eliminated, by temperature. If cultivatable land occurs at various altitudes above sea level a vertical zonation of crops similar to that described for climate and vegetation in Chapter 4 may become apparent. At lower levels (tierra caliente) crops which cannot withstand cold, such as bananas, cacao, and sugar cane, will be produced; at intermediate levels (tierra templada) corn and coffee are grown; in the next highest zone (tierra fria) only such cold-tolerant crops as wheat, potatoes, and barley can be produced; and above this no cultivation takes place but there may be some livestock grazing. In addition to the problems connected with the growing of crops, because of lack of transportation farmers may have difficulty marketing any surplus they may produce. Some upland areas may be very valuable to nearby agricultural settlements because of their usefulness for seasonal livestock grazing.

The rough terrain of mountain lands renders development of routes of transportation difficult and expensive. Although foot trails and paths for pack animals can traverse relatively steep slopes, modern highways and railroads cannot do so without great expense. Because neither motor vehicles nor railway trains can negotiate steep grades, constructing their routes through mountainous regions requires costly cuts, fills, tunnels, and bridges. When such routes are built, they usually follow low divides or passes and wind about in search of the less steep slopes. People living in mountains often are isolated from others and from the outside world. Remoteness has caused some highland peoples to remain out of contact with modern civilization and to persist in their old customs and traditions.

At present, only two types of industry seem to be favored by mountainous terrain, and neither of them is associated with large numbers of permanent inhabitants. Metallic mineral deposits may be found in abundance in highland areas, and some regions can support a sizable mining population. However, settlement based upon an exhaustible mineral resource must by its very nature be temporary and many such communities are now virtually, or actually, ghost towns. Because of their scenic beauty, wildlife population, lower temperatures, or other attractions, some mountain regions have developed the facilities for supplying goods, services, and entertainment for visitors from other parts of the world—the tourist and resort industry. Settlements devoted to such activities are almost always of limited size.

PLAINS

Plains are the landforms of the world that have low relief and elevation, and they are in most respects a strong contrast to mountains. They are probably more favorable for human occupancy than any other type of landform. Because they can be widely utilized for agriculture and do not generally present great obstacles to the development of routes of transportation, plains have become the home of a large proportion of the world's population.

Characteristics of Plains. Although the word "plain" usually implies a surface that is low and level, the criterion specifying that plains have less than 500 feet of local relief allows areas with considerable variation to be included within its limits. Some plains are almost flat, many have surfaces that are undulating to rolling, and others are so rough that they barely escape being classified as hills. Plains are made up of a variety of materials: sand and gravel, barren rock, fertile and infertile soils, snow and ice, or marsh and swamp. A few are located at elevations that are higher than mountains in other parts of the world but most are found within a thousand feet of sea level. Despite this diversity, however, plains generally do not include steeply sloping land and do not have excessive differences in elevation.

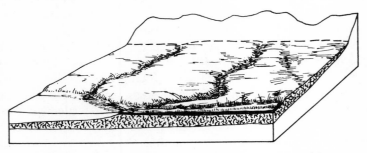

Fig. 33. Diagram of coastal plain in southern New Guinea. (ADAPTED FROM COMMONWEALTH SCIENTIFIC AND INDUSTRIAL RESEARCH OR-GANIZATION, AUSTRALIA, REPORT.)

Types of Plains. There are many ways of separating the plains of the world into subdivisions which permit more accurate description. There are significant differences among areas of low relief based upon the materials which make up the surface and other distinctions which are based upon relative roughness of the terrain. Several types of plains can be recognized according to location: *coastal plains* lie along the shorelines of continents and are usually made up of materials which were recently part of the ocean bottom (see Fig. 33); *lacustrine plains* are situated around the margins of large lakes which are slowly becoming smaller in size; *interior plains* are found far from seacoasts in the inland portions of large land masses; and *piedmont plains* consist of a number of coalescing alluvial fans lying at the foot of a mountain range. However, although there are many valid ways of classifying plains, the one which is most widely used is based upon the origins of existing features. All plains are either erosional or depositional; they result from the wearing down of an area by weathering and erosion or from the construction of a surface by deposition.

EROSIONAL PLAINS. *Erosional plains* are found where the processes of weathering have broken up the solid materials of mountains or hills and the agents of erosion have carried them away. Over long periods of time, some areas in the humid portions of the lower and middle latitudes have been reduced from mountains to hills and from hills to rolling plains by the work of running water. This type of surface develops when major streams deepen and widen their valleys while the runoff of rainfall wears away the sides and summits of ridges. These stream-eroded plains frequently have numerous remnants of the once higher elevations scattered over their surface. Such hillocks and ridges, which represent materials that were more resistant to erosion, are called *monadnocks.* Rolling areas which have gone through a long period of erosion during which mountains have been gradually worn down to form relatively level terrain are often referred to as *peneplains.*

Parts of Scandinavia, northern Russia, and Canada have plains which were formed by the scouring action of glaciers. They represent areas where glacial ice wore away the tops of ridges and filled the intervening valleys, leaving surfaces of low relief. Glacially-eroded plains are often dotted with lakes and may have broad areas with poor drainage. Many of the swamps and marshes are the remnants of shallow lakes which have gradually been drained or filled by the encroachment of vegetation.

Extensive areas with horizontal limestone rock structures that have been subject to chemical weathering and erosion by underground water form *karst plains* (see Fig. 34). Some plains of this

Fig. 34. Diagram of karst plain in northern Australia. (ADAPTED FROM COMMONWEALTH SCIENTIFIC AND INDUSTRIAL RESEARCH ORGANIZATION, AUSTRALIA, REPORT.)

type are flat, with the level terrain being interrupted only by numerous small lakes which are sink-holes that have been partially filled with water. More common karst plains are rolling-to-rough areas which have ridges and depressions arranged without any semblance of pattern; the prevailing irregularity results from the unequal dissolution of the underlying porous limestone rocks. There are few, if any, streams because most of the drainage is underground, but there are many pits and larger depressions which represent collapsed roofs of caves or areas where decomposition has taken place on the surface.

DEPOSITIONAL PLAINS. Depositional plains are formed from materials which have been laid down by running water, glaciers, winds, and ocean waters. Since those formed by the last two are extremely limited in extent, the following discussion will be restricted to the depositional plains formed by streams and glaciers.

Alluvial plains are lands which are made up of materials that have been deposited by running water. *Flood plains* are formed by the deposits of streams at times of excessive runoff and on other occasions when the speed of flow is so slow, that part of the load cannot be carried. Many rivers have low gradients in portions of their courses which cause the water to move slowly and the streams to develop winding channels with many bends or *meanders*. In time of high water the river channels may shift, cutting off curves in the courses and leaving crescent-shaped bodies of water called *ox-bow lakes* or, where former channels no longer have water, *meander scars*. The flood plains of a large stream may consist of broad stretches of level land with the highest elevations being the natural levees near the stream itself and the lowest portions the swampy land near the outer margins. A *delta plain* may form where a river carrying large amounts of alluvium flows into a relatively quiet body of water. During the delta-forming process deposits are built up at the seaward margins, in the main channel and its distributaries, and on the surface of the delta during time of flood. Many of the drainage ways which characterize deltas have built up natural levees and the intervening lands are often poorly drained. Areas around the edges of many lakes are plains that were formed from materials which were carried into the quiet waters, were sorted and deposited, and were later exposed as the margins of the lakes receded. These *lacustrine plains* are among the most level of any found on the surface of the earth. Somewhat more limited in extent than the types just described are the *piedmont alluvial plains* which are located along the bases of the great mountain ranges of many continents. They are formed where rivers emerging from a mountain slope are near enough to each other for their alluvial fans to coalesce and construct a continuous plain of stream-deposited materials.

Plains formed from glacial deposits are found on the outer margins of areas that were covered by continental ice sheets. The landforms created by these deposits were described in Chapter 5. The plains formed by ground moraines, and often referred to as *drift* or *till plains,* have level to gently rolling surfaces which at times may be interrupted by drumlins, eskers, or wide stretches of poorly drained land. Terminal and recessional moraines have irregular surfaces of greater relief, many of which are more like hills than plains. Some of the alluvial plains surrounding lakes represent materials that were deposited in enlarged lakes by the waters of melting glaciers. *Outwash plains,* which were formed from glacial debris flushed out from the margins of the ice, were laid down by water but they are intimately associated with glacial deposition. Usually they are arranged around terminal moraines like a group of fans and characteristically are flat to gently sloping in relief.

The Distribution of Plains. Although all of the great land masses of the habitable world have some area in plains, this type of terrain is most prevalent in North America, Europe, and Asiatic Russia. A considerable proportion of the total surface of South America and Australia is low and level, but only a relatively small percentage of the land of Africa and non-Russian Asia is of the plains type.

The plains of North America extend uninterrupted from the Arctic Ocean to the Gulf of Mexico. North of 40 degrees of latitude, level surfaces were produced by glacial erosion and deposition. The Great Plains along the eastern front of the Rocky Mountains are largely of alluvial origin as are large parts of the Atlantic and Gulf Coastal plains. Florida, the Yucatan Peninsula of Mexico, and numerous islands in the Caribbean have all or part of their surface in karst plains. Several small areas of alluvial lowland are found along the western side of North America.

The most important plains of South America are the alluvial lowlands of the continent's great rivers: the Magdalena-Cauca, the Orinoco, the Amazon, and the Paraguay-Parana. The Argentine pampa, which is the southernmost of the South American plains, has a surface made up of water-borne materials that have been picked up and redeposited by the wind and is a *loess plain.*

The level lands of northwestern Europe have been affected by the erosion and deposition of running water, and most of them have been greatly influenced by glaciation. The plain of northern Europe widens toward the east and in western Russia extends from the Arctic to the Black and Caspian Seas. Farther east, in central Siberia, the lowland narrows once more until in northeastern Asia it is largely limited to the Arctic coastline. The continental ice-sheet gave large parts of Siberia its level surface but the Russian plains which lie north of the Black Sea and east of the Caspian are largely of alluvial origin. The plains of southern Europe are limited to the flood plains of the larger rivers. Except for the stream-eroded plains of Manchuria, the plains of southern and eastern Asia are confined to the lower and middle portions of the great river valleys.

The African land mass is made up mostly of plateaus, with plains occupying only limited areas around the margins of the continent. The western half of Australia is a dry plateau and the extreme eastern part is dominated by hills and mountains; plains are widespread along the northern coast and in the Murray-Darling River Basin of the southeastern interior.

Man's Utilization of Plains. Although plains cover slightly more than 40 per cent of the earth's surface, they contain more than 80 per cent of the world's population. Because some are too dry, or too wet, or too cold to be suitable for use by large numbers of people, climate and associated features may be as important as relief in determining the habitability of plains.

One of the principal reasons why such a large proportion of the world's population lives upon plains is the land's adaptability for agriculture. The low relief allows mature soils to develop and soil erosion is less of a problem than upon other types of surface features. While all mature soils do not have high agricultural productivity, modern technology makes it possible for level lands to be improved by fertilization and many alluvial plains have highly fertile, although immature, soils. Low relief makes possible the use of farm machinery and the development of transportation facilities which enable farmers to market their produce.

Level terrain greatly facilitates human movement. In the absence of steep slopes and topographic barriers, highways and railroads can be constructed without excessive cost. Many plains areas are served by navigable inland waterways. The superior transportation facilities encourage trade and the growth of urban centers. Raw materials from widely separated places can be brought to cities for processing and subsequent transfer to distant markets. Since coal and petroleum deposits are commonly found in rock structures associated with level terrain (see Chapter 11), the growth of manufacturing in plains regions has been facilitated. As a result of the suitability of level land for trade and manufacturing, most of the world's great cities, as well as most of its people, are located on plains.

HILLS

Hilly regions are intermediate between mountains and plains. They are not so high or rugged as mountains, but they have surfaces with greater elevation and relief than plains. In many places their location and their features are transitional between the very rugged and the very level lands. Hilly lands present more obstacles to human occupancy than do plains but they are more favorable for settlement than mountains. They usually occur in areas which have humid climates.

Characteristics of Hilly Regions. Because of the variety of interpretations of the word "hill," the term as used in geographic study requires a precise definition. Hills are those areas which have most of their surface in slope and local relief of more than 500 and less than 2,000 feet.[1] The distinctions between low mountains and rough hills, and between rough plains and rolling hills, are not easy to make but this definition does provide the criteria if such fine lines of separation are desired.

---

[1] Not all geographers are in agreement with this distinction between hills and mountains. The figure of 2,000 feet is used here because this much relief between valley floor and summit will result in some change in climate and in natural vegetation.

Hilly regions usually have larger patches of level land and less steep slopes than mountainous regions. Vertical changes in elevation may be sufficient to create recognizable altitudinal zones of temperature and vegetation, but such differences are not prominent because either one or both of the extremes found in mountains will be missing. Both valleys and drainage divides are broader in hilly regions than in mountains.

Hills differ from plains principally in that they have more land in slope. The drainage pattern of hills is usually more intricate and streams tend to have more bends in their courses. The depositional features characteristic of plains are restricted in hilly lands to ribbons of level land along streams.

Fig. 35. Diagram of eroded hills in southern New Guinea. (ADAPTED FROM COMMONWEALTH SCIENTIFIC AND INDUSTRIAL RESEARCH ORGANIZATION, AUSTRALIA, REPORT.)

Types of Hills. Like mountains and plains, the hilly regions of the world possess sufficient individuality to warrant their being divided into subtypes. However, because hills are not so striking in appearance as mountains and not so heavily populated as plains, the classifications which have been developed for them are less precise than for other landforms.

Eroded hills are probably more widespread than any other subtype (see Fig. 35). They may represent old mountains which over the years have been gradually worn down by erosion, or foothills separating mountain ranges from lowlands. Unless the rock structures have been tilted by folding or faulting, the arrangement of ridges and valleys will be without any readily apparent pattern. Where the subsurface rocks are horizontal, or lack great variation in hardness, successively larger streams will join to form the major water course of an area much like the veins of the leaves of oak and maple trees are connected with their stems. Ridge crests and valleys will conform to this *dendritic drainage pattern.*

Structural hills have features which give definite evidence of the nature of the underlying rock structure. In areas where the subsurface layers have been inclined by folding or faulting, there will be an elongated ridge and valley arrangement. Tributary streams will join larger ones at almost right angles developing a *trellis drainage* pattern, one in which the arrangement of streams consists of a series of rectangles. Structural hills are similar to mountains formed by the same processes, but erosion has been of sufficient influence on the hills to greatly reduce the local relief.

Other types of hills have features which are similar to those described for certain types of plains, but their local relief is greater. *Glaciated hill lands* occur where ice scour or deposition has resulted in features with sufficient irregularity to prevent their being classified as plains. Wind-blown sand and dust sometimes accumulate on the leeward sides of deserts in irregular accumulations forming rough *sand dune country* and *loess hill lands.*

The Distribution of Hilly Lands. A large portion of the surface of the world that has hilly terrain is found in transitional areas located between mountains and plains or between plateaus and plains. Broad areas with eroded hills are found in the Allegheny-Cumberland hill country and the Piedmont region which lie west and east of the Appalachian Mountains of the United States. Similar features are located in the Guiana and Brazilian highlands of South America, in southeastern China, in the Indian peninsula, and in the Balkan peninsula of southern Europe. Glaciated hill lands predominate over large parts of eastern Canada, the Scandinavian peninsula, and eastern Siberia. The southern margins of the dry plateau of North Africa and the borders of the South African upland also have broad areas of hilly landscape.

Man's Utilization of Hilly Lands. Hilly terrain presents many of the obstacles to settlement that are found in mountain regions. The shortage of level land imposes severe handicaps upon agriculture and the rough surfaces make the establishment of efficient transportation networks difficult. Lines of communication usually follow the valley floors. Because of the relatively underdeveloped transportation connections with the outside world, hilly regions have tended to become areas where small groups of people have maintained old ways of living. With the improvement of highway construction techniques in modern times, many traditionally isolated areas have been linked with the outside world and profound changes have taken place.

Agricultural utilization of hilly lands has been retarded by the handicap of slope. Farming is usually concentrated on the level lands of valley bottoms and in most hilly regions the population distribution pattern corresponds to that of drainage, with the inhabitants living along the banks of streams. However, in some hilly regions population density is so great that cultivation has been forced to expand from the flat lands up the valley sides where there are problems of soil erosion and low yields per acre. Thus agricultural problems are created on lands which probably never should have been farmed in the first place. Population pressure and the unwise use of slopes have caused widespread poverty in many hilly regions of the world. The solutions to such problems will seldom be found in agricultural use of the lands; they will have to come either from moving the surplus population out of the area or by developing other ways for the population to make a living.

PLATEAUS

Plateaus are tabular uplands with relatively low relief that are occasionally interrupted by deep valleys and areas of steep slope. Usually their elevation is higher than that of plains, and they have restricted areas with local relief exceeding 500 feet. Plateaus often have a sparse population because of their low rainfall, which limits agriculture, and their occasional areas of rugged terrain which act as a deterrent to the construction of highways and railroads.

Characteristics of Plateaus. The level-to-rolling landscape which makes up most of the area of plateaus gives an outward appearance which does not differ greatly from plains. However, the streams which cross plateaus at irregular intervals have cut deeply into the upland surface and have broken it up into groups of rather isolated tablelands. (See Fig. 36.) The profiles of plateau regions show a series of level upland surfaces separated from each other by steep-sided and flat-bottomed valleys. This characteristic feature is the result of the peculiar nature of weathering and erosion in climates which are deficient in moisture. In humid regions, stream erosion wears away the angular summit edges and a large proportion of the total area is in slope, hills, and eventually stream-eroded plains. A few plateau areas are found in regions with moderate precipitation, but in these regions the rock structure is extremely resistant to erosion. Because plateaus usually have considerable elevation, they generally are bordered by steeply sloping lands on one or more sides. In some cases tablelands tower over nearby plains, in others they occupy intermediate locations between mountains and plains, and in still others they are surrounded by mountains.

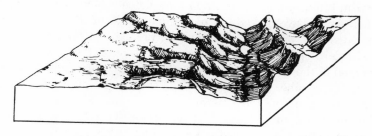

Fig. 36. Diagram of dissected plateau in northeastern Australia. (ADAPTED FROM COMMONWEALTH SCIENTIFIC AND INDUSTRIAL RESEARCH ORGANIZATION, AUSTRALIA, REPORT.)

Types of Plateaus. Plateaus do not have the great variety of terrain found in mountains and plains and therefore may be classified according to their relative location or their rock structures. According to their relationships with other types of terrain, plateaus may be described as continental, piedmont, and intermontane. *Continental plateaus* are elevated platforms of great extent that are generally unrelated to mountainous areas. Representative examples of this type are found in the tabular uplands of both northern and southern Africa and in western Australia. The tablelands of interior Brazil also belong in this category. *Piedmont plateaus* are situated between mountains and areas of level terrain or between mountains and the sea. The Patagonian region of southern Argentina and the Yunnan upland of China are plateaus of this type. *Intermontane plateaus* are areas of level land surrounded by higher surfaces in mountainous regions. Plateaus of this type, sometimes referred to as *intermontane basins,* are found in the Altiplano of the central Andes of South America, in broad areas of western North America lying between the Rockies and the Pacific coastal mountain ranges, and in the large basins contained within the great highland mass of central Asia.

Distinctions among the various plateaus of the world on the basis of rock structure are not so common as those determined by location. Some students of landforms distinguish between *horizontal* and *deformed rock plateaus* depending upon the configuration of the subsurface rock layers. Most widespread plateau areas are underlain by horizontal rock layers; deformed types involve structures that have been disturbed, then leveled by erosion, and later uplifted. A number of important plateaus have been formed where lavas have flowed out over broad areas of the earth, have cooled slowly, and have obscured the pre-existing terrain. Subsequent development of a drainage network upon the new surface resulted in the formation of deep and narrow valleys which cut it up into a number of upland areas. Examples of plateaus of this type are found in the Columbia Plateau of the northwestern United States, the Paraná Plateau of southern Brazil, and the Deccan Plateau of peninsular India. Some plateaus which originally had horizontal rock structures have experienced faulting which caused sedimentary layers to be slightly tilted and formed numerous cuestas. The steep face of the cuesta marks the edge of the fault zone. These features are common in the Colorado Plateau of the southwestern United States, the Saharan area of North Africa, and the Arabian peninsula.

The Distribution of Plateaus. Plateaus are generally located in areas with dry climates, and even two areas which are the major exceptions to this statement, central Africa and eastern Brazil, have long periods without rain each year. Most of the important plateau regions of the world have been mentioned in preceding paragraphs, but to the list should be added the intermontane plateau of central and northern Mexico, the meseta of Spain and Portugal, and the dry Anatolian and Iranian plateaus of southwestern Asia.

Man's Utilization of Plateaus. Because most of the plateaus of the world are found in arid or semiarid climates, they are not very favorable for settlement. The frequent occurrence of areas of high relief, which makes the construction of modern transportation routes expensive, has also been a deterrent to settlement. Although there is a deficiency of moisture, many plateaus have a grass cover which is capable of supporting herds of cattle, goats, sheep, or other animals, and the raising of livestock is probably the most widespread industry on this type of terrain. Crop agriculture may be present only if water is available for irrigation, and this may not be feasible even where a permanent stream crosses a plateau because the water frequently lies several hundred feet below the level upland surface. Some intermontane basins do support large agricultural populations because the mountains which surround them are partially covered with snow and ice which melt and feed streams that can be tapped for irrigation purposes. The plateaus of central Africa and eastern Brazil have climates which are classified as humid, but in both regions there is a long dry season which limits crop agriculture to a few specially favored places and the most important use of the land is for livestock grazing.

SUPPLEMENTARY READING

Bradley, John H. *Autobiography of Earth*. New York: Coward-McCann, Inc., 1935.

Cotton, C. A. *Landscape, as Developed by the Processes of Normal Erosion*. 2nd ed. New York: John Wiley & Sons, Inc., 1948.

Croneis, Carey, and Krumbein, William C. *Down to Earth*. Chicago: University of Chicago Press, 1936.

Davis, William M. *Geographical Essays*. New York: Dover Publications, Inc., 1954. (Originally published in 1909 by Ginn & Co., Boston.)

Gamow, George. *Biography of the Earth*. New York: Viking Press, 1948.

Leet, L. D., and Judson, Sheldon. *Physical Geology*. 3rd ed. Englewood Cliffs, N.J.: Prentice-Hall, Inc., 1965.

Lobeck, A. K. *Geomorphology*. New York: McGraw-Hill Book Co., Inc., 1939.

Longwell, Chester R.; Knopf, Adolph; and Flint, Richard F. *Outlines of Physical Geology*. 2nd ed. New York: John Wiley & Sons, Inc., 1941.

Putnam, William C. *Geology*. New York: Oxford University Press, 1964.

Thornbury, W. D. *Principles of Geomorphology*. New York: John Wiley & Sons, Inc., 1954.

7

Natural Vegetation

Although man's use of the land has greatly modified the native vegetation in many parts of the world, the study of plant distribution patterns and the factors which affect them is helpful in explaining differences between areas of the earth. Natural vegetation is one of the most prominent features of the physical landscape of an area, particularly in underpopulated lands, and is a good representation of the total natural environment. In regions which have few or no weather stations, the vegetation cover gives a reliable indication of the nature of climatic conditions. Where no soil surveys have been made, plant associations can be utilized to make valid assumptions concerning the fertility of the soil. For man, forests and grasses are often the resources which provide the basic means of support for population groups.

ENVIRONMENTAL CONDITIONS AFFECTING PLANT GROWTH

The flora of a region depends upon a combination of the climatic, slope, and soil conditions. Broad vegetation types are determined to a great extent by climatic conditions, while variations in vegetation within the major climate zones are largely the result of differences in slope and in underlying earth materials.

Climatic Conditions. A comparison of maps showing the distribution of climatic types and of natural vegetation types throughout the world reveals the close correspondence between climatic patterns and floral communities (see Figs. 23 and 37, pages 56 and 126). The plant associations of a region are largely a reflection of temperature, moisture, and light conditions.

TEMPERATURE. The many species of plants that are found over the surface of the earth react to heat and cold in different ways.

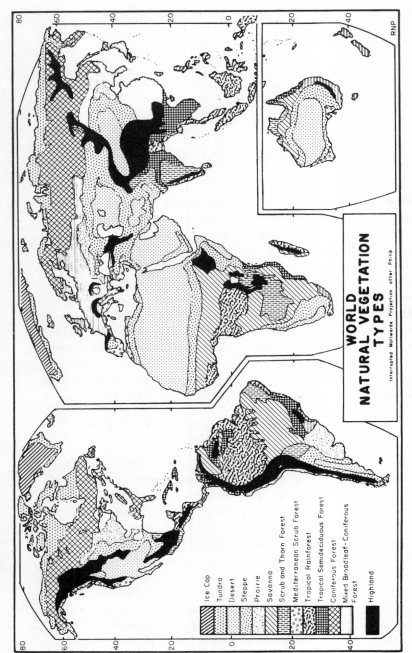

WORLD
NATURAL VEGETATION
TYPES

Interrupted Mollweide Projection after Philip

Ice Cap
Tundra
Desert
Steppe
Prairie
Savanna
Scrub and Thorn Forest
Mediterranean Scrub Forest
Tropical Rainforest
Tropical Semideciduous Forest
Coniferous Forest
Mixed Broadleaf-Coniferous Forest
Highland

Fig. 37.

RNP

Although 32° F. temperature (freezing point) is generally considered to be the absolute minimum for vegetation growth, plants usually cease to grow when air temperatures are below 42° F., and some cannot exist in areas where the lowest temperature is several degrees higher. The palm and other tropical trees and shrubs are seldom found where monthly averages fall below 50° F., many mid-latitude plants are not found poleward of the 32° isotherm for the coldest month of the year, and the 50° isotherm for the warmest month of the year approximates the poleward limit of forests. Most plants have optimum temperatures for growth and critical temperatures above and below which they cannot survive; if the temperature in an area is not highly favorable to their growth, other species will crowd them out. A large number of vegetation types complete their life cycle during a period of less than 365 days and the length of their growth period will greatly affect their distribution.

MOISTURE. Since all plants require some moisture, the amount and seasonal distribution of precipitation is an important determinant of the type of vegetation an area will have. Humid regions generally have forest growth, arid regions have desert types of vegetation, and intermediate regions have grasslands or scrub forest. However, the effects of precipitation upon vegetation cover cannot be measured only in terms of the annual amount of rainfall, but depend also on when the precipitation occurs. Some climate zones, notably the dry summer subtropical, have most of their precipitation during their cooler winter season and their vegetation is more characteristic of dry lands than would be expected from the annual amount of moisture received. This low *precipitation effectiveness* is also characteristic of many tropical and subtropical regions where much of the warm season rainfall evaporates and thus is unavailable for plant growth.

LIGHT. The amount and duration of sunlight is a decisive factor in the development of natural vegetation in an area. Sunlight is essential for plant nutrition through photosynthesis, and comparatively few plants can be cultivated in deep shade. (Among the exceptions are edible fungi such as mushrooms which require humid air, 58°-60° F. temperature, and darkness.)

Edaphic Conditions. The characteristics of soil and slope which affect the natural vegetation of areas are referred to as *edaphic conditions.* Where the underlying rock or parent material is especially porous, such as sand or limestone, surface water soaks into the ground so rapidly that much of it cannot be utilized by plants. As a result, an area which otherwise has sufficient precipitation for trees may have a grassland cover, or areas having enough rainfall for grass may be dominated by desert plants. Similar situations may occur on steep slopes where, because of the excessive run-off of rainfall, much of the precipitation cannot be utilized for plant growth.

PLANT ASSOCIATIONS

From the point of view of geography there are three major plant associations which result from combinations of the climatic and edaphic conditions: forests, grasslands, and deserts. The most important element affecting the distribution of the three contrasting types is moisture. Each major association may be subdivided into two or more types, depending upon the temperature of the environment as well as upon the amount and distribution of precipitation. The number of species which constitute any one of the major associations may be great, but if we wish to distinguish world patterns we must focus our attention upon dominant types rather than individual plants. The plant associations described in the following paragraphs are those which cover broad areas and can be mapped on a world scale. However, there are many local variations of the general associations, induced by the local edaphic conditions.

FORESTS

Since trees demand more moisture than grasses or desert vegetation, the distribution of forests corresponds to that of lands with humid climates. (See Fig. 37.) Each of the three major types of forest may be subdivided into several subtypes.

Tropical Forests.   Low latitude or tropical forests are found in regions with rainy tropical climates and on the humid margins of areas with wet and dry tropical climates.

Tropical Rainforests.   Lands which have heavy rainfall and high temperatures throughout the year are covered with a dense forest of broadleaf trees called tropical rainforest or *selva.* Since there is no dormant season imposed by either drought or cold,

individual trees do not lose all of their leaves at the same time and the forest is *evergreen*. The trees are closely spaced with their crowns joined overhead, making it difficult for sunlight to reach the ground, and the forest floor is often remarkably clear of undergrowth. Although underbrush is usually found only beside streams and in other places where sunlight can penetrate the overhead canopy, there are numerous clinging plants and vines which encircle tree trunks and branches; some are *parasites* which feed upon the sap of the plant upon which they grow and others are *epiphytes* which are supported by but do not feed upon other plants. Many of the trees of the selva reach heights in excess of 100 feet and there are often several layers or tiers of trees grouped at lower elevations. One remarkable feature of this vegetation type is the large number of individual species of trees, some useful to man and some not, scattered widely throughout the forest. Among the valuable trees are mahogany, teak, sandalwood, Spanish cedar, and rubber. However, individual species of trees do not grow close together in solid stands, and the wood of many varieties has such a high specific gravity that cut logs will not float. The resulting problems of widely scattered supply and difficult transportation have hindered man's attempt to utilize the resources of the selva.

Tropical Semideciduous Forest. Many parts of the rainy low latitudes have a short but distinct dry season. The total annual rainfall may be heavy, but the short dry, or less wet, period causes the forest to experience seasonal change, and many of the trees lose their leaves at the same time. This results in what is termed a tropical semideciduous forest. Many of the species of the selva are present but the tree growth is more irregular and in places where the sunlight can penetrate to the forest floor there is a dense undergrowth of bushes, shrubs, weeds, and vines, called *jungle*. Bamboo thickets are common in many forests of this type. Generally the trees are farther apart, smaller in size, and of lower height than in the selva, but in areas receiving heavy rainfall from monsoon winds the height, size, and density of the vegetation growth may exceed that of the true tropical rainforest. These areas are often referred to as *monsoon rainforest*.

Tropical Scrub and Thorn Forest. On the margins of the rainy tropics where the dry season is longer and the amount of rainfall is lower, the vegetation cover consists of low trees, bushes, and bunch grass and is called *tropical scrub and thorn forest*. In such areas, relatively less moisture and high evaporation rates make it necessary for most plants to adapt to a shortage of water. Plants which are capable of adjusting themselves to a scarcity of moisture are said to be *xerophytic*. Trees and bushes have small waxy-coated leaves and thick bark which lessen the loss of moisture through transpiration. Many are bare of foliage much of the year. Some plants may have thorns instead of leaves, and many have extensive root systems which permit them to utilize the rainfall of a wide area or have deep tap roots which go far underground in search of moisture.

Mid-latitude Forests. Poleward from the tropics, in humid climates, seasonal fluctuations in both temperature and precipitation cause a considerable variety of forest types.

MEDITERRANEAN SCRUB FOREST. The lands with dry summer subtropical climates have a vegetation cover that is both evergreen and dominated by broadleaf trees. Since the warm season has very little precipitation, plants must adapt to the deficiency of moisture. The vegetation is xerophytic in nature and resembles in many ways the tropical scrub forest previously described. Trees tend to be small, gnarled, and widely spaced. Evergreen oaks, myrtle, laurel, and olive are among the most common varieties. There is usually a low growth of stunted shrubs and bushes, such as is called *chaparral* in California and *maqui* in the lands surrounding the Mediterranean Sea. Grasses usually are scarce, except for some areas in California which are covered with bunch grass. Since the regions with these environmental conditions have been so greatly exploited by man, areas having this type of vegetation in its natural state are not extensive.

BROADLEAF FORESTS. The poleward margins of the selva and tropical semideciduous forests give way to a vegetation type that consists mainly of broadleaf deciduous trees. Dominant species differ widely from continent to continent and according to the severity of the winter season, but these hardwood forests composed of trees that seasonally lose their leaves are the predominant vegetation over broad areas having humid subtropical and humid continental climates. The interior of the southeastern United States, for example, has a broadleaf forest of oak, chestnut, and poplar, but farther north the species are principally hickory, maple, and oak.

MIXED BROADLEAF-CONIFEROUS FORESTS. Although broadleaf trees predominate in the forests of the middle latitudes, in most areas there is a mixture of broadleaf and coniferous species. Under the edaphic conditions of the humid subtropics of the United States, particularly on the poor and sandy soils of coastal regions, pine and other needle-bearing species are more numerous than hardwoods. In the poleward portions of the humid continental climates of North America, where winters are more severe, stands of spruce, fir, and hemlock are interspersed among the predominant oak, hickory, and maple. Some of the most valuable forests of the middle latitudes are found in the coniferous stands of the mild, rainy west coasts of the United States and Canada. Here, large and dense clusters of Douglas fir, redwood, cedar, and spruce constitute a great timber resource. Other mid-latitude marine lands may have a heavy forest growth but the trees are often broadleaf species and are less valuable than those found in similar climates in North America.

Northern Coniferous Forests. Along the northern margins of the humid continental climates of North America and Eurasia the increasing length and severity of the winters make it difficult for broadleaf trees to thrive and coniferous varieties are more numerous. The resulting forest is referred to as *northern coniferous forest, boreal forest,* or *taiga.* Pine, spruce, fir, hemlock, and other needle-bearing types dominate the landscape. Some quick-growing broadleaf species such as willow, aspen, and birch are found along streams and in other favorable sites, but the forest is essentially coniferous. Unlike those of the selva and mid-latitude forests, the trees are generally rather small in size, widely spaced, and the number of species is limited. Except on the southern borders where growing seasons are longer and trees are consequently larger, the taiga is not particularly valuable as a timber resource. However, the trees of these forests are widely utilized for wood pulp and paper manufacture.

GRASSLANDS

Grasslands are transitional between forests and deserts. They generally do not have sufficient precipitation to support a forest cover but there is enough moisture for grasses or a mixture of grasses and trees. The commonly recognized types of grasslands are (1) *savannas* or tropical grasslands, (2) *prairies* or tall grasslands of the middle latitudes, and (3) *steppes* or short grasslands of the middle latitudes.

Savannas. Tropical grasslands occupy an intermediate position between tropical forests and tropical deserts and are typical of areas with wet and dry tropical climates. Savannas are of many types, depending upon the height of the grasses and the nature of the accompanying tree growth, both of which are greatly affected by the availability of moisture. Tropical grasslands almost always include scattered trees, and along streams which cross savannas usually there is sufficient water for a *gallery forest*. Near the borders of the tropical forests, where precipitation is greater, grasses may be six to eight feet in height and the savanna is interspersed with a fairly close scattering of low trees. Farther poleward nearer the deserts, where there is less rainfall, grasses are much shorter and trees are smaller and farther apart. On the margins of the dry lands savanna grasses become coarser, shorter, and form a less complete cover over the earth's surface. Because of the rainfall pattern in these areas, the savannas are lush and green during the wet season and parched and brown for the remainder of the year. The local names that have been applied to savanna lands in South America and Africa (see Chapter 4) do not indicate any essential difference in grassland type.

Prairies. Along the subhumid margins of mid-latitude forests in several parts of the world, the natural vegetation consists of wide expanses of grasses called prairies. These grasses grow from three to eight feet in height and are deep-rooted and closely spaced. Except for the forests which border streams in these areas, the prairies are generally without trees. The origins of the prairies are somewhat of a puzzle to scientists because these grasslands extend rather far into climates which appear to have sufficient moisture to support forests, and when trees are planted in such regions they will usually grow without great difficulty. Some scholars believe that the prairies are ancient cultural features brought about by repeated burning of the vegetation cover by primitive peoples. The most famous areas of tall mid-latitude grassland are the prairies of the midwestern United States and the *pampas* of northern Argentina, Uruguay, and southern Brazil. Other areas with this type of vegetation are found in Hungary, southern European Russia, and in the plains of Manchuria.

Steppes. The humid margins of desert regions have a short grass type vegetation which is commonly called *steppe.* In comparison with prairies, steppe grasses are much shorter and have a tendency to grow in clusters, as *bunch grass.* On their humid margins steppes serve as transitional zones with prairies or in some instances with forests. Although the distinction is not usually made, it also seems appropriate to refer to the shorter grasses on the dry margins of savannas as steppes.

DESERTS

The term *desert* as used here applies to areas which have a sparse vegetation cover or are barren because of a deficiency of moisture. Tundra areas, which border polar seas, are deserts of cold and their vegetation has many of the features of the more commonly recognized deserts of dryness. The icecaps and wastelands of the polar regions are devoid of vegetation and are deserts.

Dry Deserts. Contrary to popular belief, the deserts which extend from low latitude west coasts toward mid-latitude continental interiors have very little area that is completely barren of vegetation. Individual plants are widely scattered and all have one or more characteristics which enable them to exist for long periods without rain. There are *perennials* which have very short growth periods, and *annuals* which quickly complete their life cycle when moisture is available. Cacti have thorns which serve a protective function and have tissues which enable them to store water during extended droughts. Bushes and shrubs have small waxy or hairy leaves, thick bark, and extensive root systems which conserve moisture or permit it to be gathered from large areas. The plants of the dry deserts are xerophytic, or structurally adapted to dryness, and they seldom form a complete cover of the earth's surface.

Tundra. The broad areas of grasses, bushes, mosses, and stunted trees, called *tundra,* lie between subarctic forests and polar seas. As in dry deserts, the vegetation does not form a continuous cover of the surface and all plants are xerophytic.

Tundra plants must adapt to a shortage of moisture not because there is no water present but because the water is usually frozen and unavailable for plant growth most of the year. During the short warm season in tundra regions when plants may grow, their growth is handicapped by an excess of moisture resulting from the thawing of the frozen subsoils and the slow rate of evaporation of this moisture.

HIGHLAND VEGETATION

The vertical zonation of climates in mountainous regions is strongly reflected in the distribution of the various types of natural vegetation. The altitudinal zones which are recognized (see Chapter 4) apply to both climate and vegetation. The vertical banding which is common in all highland regions is most conspicuous in well-populated areas in the tropics because the contrast between low elevations and mountain peaks is greater than in higher latitudes and the variation in crops corresponds to differences in altitude. In many parts of the tropics the *tierra caliente* is the zone of bananas, cacao, sugar cane, and manioc (a root crop similar to a large sweet potato that is widely grown as a food crop); the *tierra templada* is the zone of corn, coffee, and subtropical fruit; the *tierra fria* is the zone of wheat, barley, potatoes, and temperate fruit; and the zone of mountain meadows is too cold for crop agriculture but is often utilized for the pasturage of livestock. In middle and high latitudes the most significant vegetation changes occur at the tree line and the snow line, both of which vary in accordance with latitude and precipitation as well as altitude.

SUPPLEMENTARY READING

Cain, Stanley A. *Foundations of Plant Geography*. New York: Harper & Brothers, 1944.

Dansereau, Pierre. *Biogeography*. New York: Ronald Press, Inc., 1957.

Daubenmire, Rexford F. *Plants and Environment*. 2nd ed. New York: John Wiley & Sons, Inc., 1959.

Eyre, S. R. *Vegetation and Soils: A World Picture*. Chicago: Aldine Publishing Co., 1963.

Gleason, H. A., and Cronquist, A. *The Natural Geography of Plants.* New York: Columbia University Press, 1964.

Grass. The Yearbook of Agriculture, 1948, U.S. Department of Agriculture. Washington, D.C.: Government Printing Office, 1948.

McDougall, W. B. *Plant Ecology.* Philadelphia: Lea and Febiger, 1949.

Newbigin, Marion I. *Plant and Animal Geography.* Rev. ed. New York: E. P. Dutton & Co., 1948.

Trees. The Yearbook of Agriculture, 1949, U.S. Department of Agriculture. Washington, D.C.: Government Printing Office, 1949.

8

Soils

Soil and water are two of the earth's most valuable natural resources. Both are necessary for the production of the food which sustains human life, and one is virtually useless without the other. Soils may be defined as unconsolidated materials on the earth's surface that are capable of supporting plant life. They are formed from both mineral and organic materials, and their composition is influenced by the combined factors of parent material, climate, vegetation, and relief. Soils differ widely from place to place over the surface of the earth.

SOIL CHARACTERISTICS

Many of the physical properties of soils can be distinguished without the aid of instruments. Even the untrained observer can see that soils differ from each other in color, size of particles, and the manner in which the individual particles group themselves together. Not so apparent is the fact that the soil in most places changes in character with depth and consists of a series of distinct layers which can be analyzed and classified.

Soil Profile. As soil is formed from broken-up particles of the earth's crust, called *regolith* or *parent material,* a great many processes take place. Air and water enter the spaces between particles, many forms of plant and animal life become commingled with the particles, and from the interaction of air, water, and organic substances with the parent material the process of soil formation begins. As the soil formation processes evolve, definite layers develop near the earth's surface. These layers, known as *horizons,* differ from each other chemically and physically, and a vertical cross section of these horizons constitutes the *soil profile.* From the earth's surface downward, four horizons are recog-

136

nized and are identified by the letters A, B, C, and D. The upper layer, or A-horizon, is the zone where organic matter accumulates on the surface and where the semi-decayed plant and animal material called *humus* is found. This is the layer from which water soaking into the ground may remove material by either chemical or physical action. The B-horizon, the second layer, is the zone where material removed from above accumulates. It is usually composed of finer particles and forms a more compact substance than the layer above. The two upper zones are the most important portions of the soil profile. The C-horizon consists of broken-up fragments of the parent material and the D-horizon is the unaltered parent material.

Soil Texture. The size of the particles found in a soil—their fineness or coarseness—determines its *texture*. Texture is an important aspect of soil study, for it is the texture which determines how readily the soil can absorb water, heat, and air, and can make mineral elements available for plant growth. Although no soil will fall precisely into one textural group, the major categories of soil texture in decreasing order of size of particles are: (1) *sand*—individual grains can be distinguished easily and feel gritty to the fingers; (2) *silt*—individual particles can scarcely be seen and the soil feels and looks like flour; and (3) *clay*—individual particles cannot be seen without the aid of a microscope. The major soil types have varying proportions of particles of different sizes. Among the more common combinations of particles are those known as sandy loam, fine sand, coarse sandy loam, clay loam, silty clay, and sandy clay.

Soil Structure. The manner in which individual particles in a soil group themselves together is referred to as soil *structure*. In sandy soils, the particles do not cling together; clays tend to form in lumps or clods; and in some soils the particles combine into rounded aggregates of varying size. The structure of a soil gives an indication of how it will produce under cultivation.

Soil Color. Color is probably the most easily observed soil characteristic and is one of the most significant. Color gives insight into the physical and chemical processes which have formed a soil and may be an indication of its fertility. The range of color in soils includes white or light gray, yellow, red, and brown to black. In humid regions, a red or reddish brown color may indicate the presence of iron oxides in the soil; a white color may denote a lack of them. Dark brown and black usually indicate the presence of large amounts of organic material. In arid regions, whitish colors ordinarily give evidence of a high concentration of soluble salts, a characteristic of alkalinity.

SOIL FORMING PROCESSES

The soil of an area is the result of a long evolution in which the parent material is subjected to the physical and chemical action of percolating water and to the influence of many kinds of living organisms. Comparisons of soil maps of the world with those for climate and natural vegetation suggest the close relationship among these three elements of the natural environment.

Control by Parent Material. The composition of the parent material is a primary cause of local differences in soils. Climate, vegetation, and other factors may influence the development of similarities in soils over broad areas, but they seldom completely obliterate the effects of differences in parent material. Some parent materials may be significantly changed by the physical and chemical processes of soil formation but others, particularly sand, may strongly resist alteration. Soils whose parent material resists change do not have well-developed profiles and are referred to as *azonal soils*.

Analyses of parent material provide sharper, more detailed patterns of the arrangement of soils, but these patterns cannot generally be shown on maps of continental or world scale.

Leaching. Leaching is the process by which water percolating downward in the soil, or moving over the surface of the soil, chemically removes soluble minerals from one place and deposits them elsewhere. It takes place generally in humid climates where water is abundant. Since solution occurs more rapidly at high temperatures, leaching also occurs more often in warm than in cool climates. In soils of rainy climates the A-horizons are usually deficient in soluble minerals because these have been dissolved out and concentrated in the B-horizon.

Eluviation. Eluviation involves the mechanical removal of particles from upper layers of the soil by moving water and the deposition of these particles elsewhere. Fine material may be carried out in suspension from the A-horizon, leaving a coarse upper layer, and be deposited in the *B*-horizon which then becomes a dense and compact zone of fine materials. Where this occurs, the closely consolidated material is known as *hardpan* or *pan layer*. Like leaching, eluviation is more common in rainy climates.

Humus Accumulation. *Humus*, which is semi-decayed organic matter, accumulates where plant and animal debris collects at the surface of the earth and bacterial action does not destroy it too rapidly. It is the presence of decomposed organic materials that causes soil to differ from parent material, but if decay is complete there is no humus. Because humus contains nitrogen which is essential to plant growth, the amount of organic matter in a soil is often an indication of its fertility, particularly on well-drained lands. Excessive amounts of humus usually contribute to a high degree of acidity. The amount of organic matter in soil is strongly influenced by the vegetation cover of an area; the largest amounts of organic matter accumulate in soils under grasslands cover, and broadleaf forests supply more organic matter than do coniferous forests.

Biological Factors. Living organisms transfer humus to the soil and mix it with mineral components. Bacteria and other micro-organisms cause the decay of organic matter and contribute to the mixing of organic and mineral substances, and their remains add to the humus content of the soil. The roots of plants growing into the soil help to make the earth porous, and when the plants die their remains also add to the humus content of the soil. Earthworms and some burrowing animals contribute to the mixing of the various components which are present in soils.

MATURE SOILS

The several soil-forming processes acting upon parent material have resulted in the formation of many different soils over the surface of the earth. The controls of relief, earth material, climate, and vegetation produce such an endless variety of soils that to classify them completely on a world-wide scale would be impossible. However, if attention is focused upon those soils which have remained undisturbed for a long period of time under similar conditions of vegetation and climate, it is possible to arrive at a meaningful world classification. Such a system recognizes broad

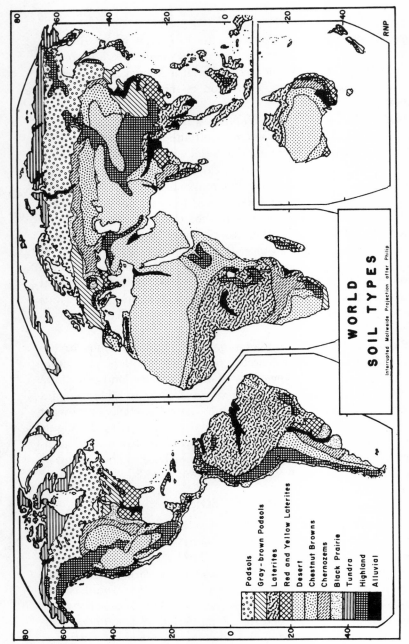

WORLD
SOIL TYPES

Interrupted Mollweide Projection after Philip

Podsols
Gray-brown Podsols
Laterites
Red and Yellow Laterites
Desert
Chestnut Browns
Chernozems
Black Prairie
Tundra
Highland
Alluvial

Fig. 38.

categories of *mature soil* types, which are soils that have been formed on well-drained land, under similar conditions of climate and vegetation, and which have well-developed profiles. The several types of mature soils are often called the *great soil groups* or *zonal soils*. They do not include *intrazonal soils* which are subtypes resulting from variation in parent material or relief, or *azonal soils* such as alluvium which have had insufficient time to form well-developed profiles.

WORLD SOIL TYPES

Mature soils—or zonal soils, or the great soil groups—occur over broad areas of the earth. They have well-developed profiles, have been in place for long periods of time, reflect the influence of climate and vegetation, and are most widespread on relatively level surfaces where the parent material is not of extreme structure or composition. The world distribution of the principal soil types is shown in Figure 38.[1]

Laterites. The lateritic soils, or laterites, are common to areas with rainy tropical and wet and dry tropical climates and selva or savanna type vegetation. The surface layer is a dark red to brown color, is coarse in texture, has a high percentage of iron and other insoluble minerals and a low percentage of humus. Under conditions of heavy precipitation and high temperatures both leaching and eluviation have been intense. Rapid decay of organic matter under such climatic conditions greatly retards the accumulation of humus. The *B*-horizon, which has an even deeper color than the surface layer, consists of fine particles and is often very compact. The laterites are deficient in both mineral and organic plant foods and do not stand up well under continuous cultivation, particularly for shallow-rooted crops.

Red and Yellow Laterites. Similar to the laterites but more widespread in extent and of greater utility for agriculture are the red and yellow lateritic soils. They extend from the rainy tropics well into the humid subtropical regions. Although they have been subjected to the same soil-forming processes as the laterites the

---

[1] Figure 38 is essentially a map of the zonal, or mature, soils of the world. Several areas of alluvium, azonal soils, have been included because they are large enough to be mapped at this scale.

evolution has not been so complete, and conditions of climate and vegetation are somewhat different. The A-horizon is lighter in color with yellows often predominating, the surface consists of finer particles, and the organic content is somewhat higher than in the laterites. Although they cannot be described as fertile the red and yellow laterites can be utilized successfully for agriculture if they are handled properly and are fertilized frequently.

Gray-brown Podsols Soils.   The mid-latitude forests of the humid continental climates have soils that are intermediate between those which have evolved through lateritic processes and the podsols of the northern coniferous forests. These gray-brown podsolic soils have a greater accumulation of humus than those found on either their poleward or equatorward margins and have been less affected by leaching and eluviation. The surface layer is grayish brown in color, has suffered some removal of soluble minerals, and contains a moderate supply of organic matter. The B-horizon is usually a deeper brown than the upper layer and is made up of finely textured material. Although the gray-brown forest soils are considered to be of only moderate fertility, under careful management they may be highly productive for crop agriculture. Much of the farm economy of the northeastern United States, western Europe, and northern China is based upon soils of this group.

Podsols.   The typical mature soils of regions with subarctic climate and taiga vegetation, called podsols, have a light gray A-horizon, a dark brown subsurface layer, and generally low productivity. The resinous accumulation of debris from the coniferous forest retards bacterial action and decay and transforms water soaking through it into a mild acid. This acidic solution removes soluble minerals such as iron and aluminum from the upper horizon, leaving a loose, friable, grayish white material that is low in humus, acidic, and without structure. The B-horizon contains the minerals which have been leached from above and deposited in a dense and compact *hardpan.* When cultivated, the podsols quickly lose their small organic content, rapidly decline in productivity, and may be subject to severe wind erosion.

Black Prairie Soils.   Along the less rainy margins of the mid-latitude forests where prairie grasslands are the dominant vegetation type, the soils conform to the change in moisture and vegetation. The heavy grass cover provides a large amount of organic material and results in dark brown to black soils that are of high fertility for most agricultural purposes. These soils are usually very deep and the dark color continues into the *B*-horizon. Although the black prairie soils are subject to some leaching, the removal of minerals is not so excessive as in the forested areas with heavier rainfall. The most widespread area of soils with these characteristics is in the central part of the United States, particularly in the Corn Belt, but other examples are found in the grass and forest transition zones of east central South America and of eastern Europe.

Chernozems. In the areas found along the dry margins of the prairies and the humid margins of the steppes, the distinguishing characteristic of mature soils is an accumulation of alkaline minerals in the *B*-horizon. These limy deposits result from the evaporation of water seeping downward after periods of drought. The surface layers under grassland vegetation are high in humus and, like the prairie soils, are dark brown to black in color. Since the chernozems are associated with regions of low rainfall they are less leached and have a higher mineral content than the soils on their humid borders. For most agricultural crops these soils have high fertility. Outstanding areas with chernozem soils are found from western and central Texas north to the plains provinces of Canada in North America, from the pampa of Argentina north into Paraguay in South America, and from the Ukraine of European Russia eastward into central Siberia.

Chestnut Brown Soils. The chestnut brown soils which occupy the transition zone between steppes and deserts have many of the characteristics of the chernozems. They reach their greatest extent in the great plains of North America and in the dry zone of interior Eurasia. Because of the lesser amounts of rainfall the vegetation cover is not so abundant, the humus content is lower, and the color is somewhat lighter. Evaporation is very effective in the chestnut brown soils; the lime accumulation layer is more prominent and generally nearer the surface.

Desert Soils. The soils which develop under the sparse vegetation and low precipitation of desert regions are light in color, low in organic content, and high in soluble minerals. The color and mineral content may be strongly affected by the nature of the parent material from which the soils are formed. The A-horizon is usually shallow and the lime accumulation is near or at the surface. Alkaline content is sometimes so high that only a few salt-resistant plants can grow. If the mineral content is not excessive, desert soils may become very fertile under irrigation.

Tundra Soils. The climatic conditions of the lands bordering the polar seas, mainly in the Arctic region, preclude widespread development of mature soils. Low evaporation rates and the permanently frozen subsurface layers cause the soils of broad areas to be waterlogged most of the time. The low temperatures retard the decomposition of what little organic matter might be provided by the sparse vegetation cover. On sites that are well drained, and where there is some modification of the harsh climatic conditions, there are mature soils that greatly resemble the podsols.

Soils in Mountain Regions. Since mature soils develop only where the earth materials remain undisturbed for long periods of time, there are no typical mature soils of mountain regions. On widespread areas of steep slope, surface material is constantly eroded and carried down to the valleys, and a soil profile does not develop. In general, valley floors in highlands do not develop mature profiles because of the frequent deposition of materials from the surrounding slopes. Where mature soils do develop in large mountain basins, they tend to have characteristics that conform to the altitudinal climate and vegetation zone in which they are situated.

SUPPLEMENTARY READING

Bennett, Hugh H. *Elements of Soil Conservation.* 2nd ed. New York: McGraw-Hill Book Co., Inc., 1955.

Buckman, Harry O., and Brady, Nyle C. *The Nature and Properties of Soils.* 6th ed. rev. New York: Macmillan Co., 1960.

Bunting, B. T. *The Geography of Soil.* London: Hutchinson and Co., 1965.

Eyre, S. R. *Vegetation and Soils: A World Picture.* Chicago: Aldine Publishing Co., 1963.

Jenny, Hans. *Factors of Soil Formation.* New York: McGraw-Hill Book Co., Inc., 1941.

Kellogg, Charles E. *The Soils That Support Us.* New York: Macmillan Co., 1941.

Soil. The Yearbook of Agriculture, 1957, U.S. Department of Agriculture. Washington, D.C.: Government Printing Office, 1957.

Soils and Men. The Yearbook of Agriculture, 1938, U.S. Department of Agriculture. Washington, D.C.: Government Printing Office, 1938.

9

Water Resources

Water is an indispensable natural resource—no form of life can exist without it. Although the amount of moisture present in the zone between the upper layers of the earth's crust and the outer limits of the atmosphere is constant, there is great variation in the availability of water from one part of the world to another. People who live in regions which have an abundant supply of water often fail to understand the problems of those who live where water is scarce. The great demands that modern civilization places upon this resource are causing increased emphasis to be placed upon its conservation.

THE IMPORTANCE OF WATER

The basic use of water is for drinking purposes, for man cannot exist without it; the human body is more than 70 per cent water by weight. Water is required for innumerable household activities. It is necessary for the production of crops; most actively growing plants contain more liquid than solid matter, and regions with low precipitation must have irrigation water available if crops are to flourish. The seas, lakes, and streams of the world supply man with fish for food. Modern industrial growth requires quantities of water for many purposes: for washing raw materials, for cooling, for the minerals that are present in solution in water bodies. Early manufacturing plants utilized the water wheel as a source of power and much of the energy used in modern factories is obtained from electricity generated by the force of falling water. Through the ages natural waterways have greatly facilitated the movement of goods and people, and despite the development of land and air transportation facilities, water routes still carry a large part of the commodities that enter

146

world trade. With increased leisure time available to large numbers of people, the establishment of specialized recreational facilities has focused attention upon places that have the resources for swimming, fishing, boating, and other water-oriented sports.

The Hydrologic Cycle

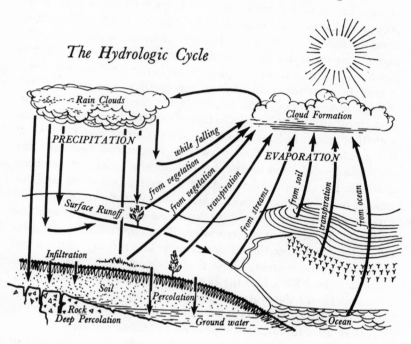

Fig. 39. *The hydrologic cycle.* (From *Water*, The Yearbook of Agriculture, 1955, United States Department of Agriculture.)

WATER SUPPLY

Water exists in nature in three forms: in a solid state as snow and ice, as a gas in the form of water vapor, and as a liquid in quantities varying from tiny water droplets in clouds to the vast accumulations found in seas and oceans. Although the water supply of an area generally depends upon the amount, seasonal distribution, and type of precipitation which it receives, certain other conditions are of considerable significance in determining the total amount of moisture available.

The Hydrologic Cycle. The moisture on or near the earth's surface and in the atmosphere does not vary greatly from year to year but exists in a giant circulatory system known as the hydrologic or water cycle (see Fig. 39). This cycle has no beginning or ending, but to describe the cycle we begin with the waters of the oceans and seas that cover three-fourths of the globe. Moisture from the oceans is evaporated into the atmosphere and is lifted to higher elevations by the movement of air. Winds transport the moisture-laden air from over the oceans across land masses where it may be condensed and fall to the earth as precipitation. Although some precipitation occurs in the form of snow, hail, or sleet, most of this solid precipitation eventually melts and joins with that which falls as rain to become running water. Some of the precipitation over land masses is evaporated back into the atmosphere and some soaks into the ground where it becomes available for growing plants. After the vegetation cover and the ground have been moistened, much of the water runs off the land surface into streams, where it may cause erosion and contribute to floods. In many areas, considerable quantities of water permeate far into the earth and slowly percolate through springs and seeps to maintain stream flow during dry periods. The streams eventually lead back into the oceans where the water originated. To comprehend the water resources of the world, we must first understand these various routes which water takes as it returns to the ocean after it has fallen upon earth as precipitation.

The hydrologic cycle may operate differently in various parts of the world. The precipitation that takes place over large water bodies abruptly abbreviates the cycle. In certain instances, not all runoff water is returned directly into the oceans. Some rainfall is evaporated back into the atmosphere immediately, and some is detained in lakes and swamps or is confined within the rocks of the earth's crust. In high latitude or high altitude areas, large quantities of precipitation are retained in glaciers and snowfields.

Atmospheric Moisture. In some parts of the world, the water supply is curtailed by the loss of moisture directly into the atmosphere through evaporation and through transpiration by plants. Evaporation and transpiration reduce the amount of water that is added to the ground supply by precipitation and lessen the quantity available for human use. In many areas, the annual loss of water into the atmosphere by these processes exceeds the total precipitation, and in others this condition of moisture loss exists for several months of each year. Where and when this excessive evaporation and transpiration take place, the supply of water in the soil is not replenished and any attempts to carry on agriculture must be supplemented by irrigation. As methods of artificially inducing rainfall become perfected, atmospheric moisture may become a water resource of considerable potential. In some parts of the world the air contains sufficient quantities of water vapor to support a vegetation cover that can be utilized for livestock pasturage, even though there is little actual precipitation in those areas.

Underground Water. Some of the water which falls upon the earth's surface seeps underground into spaces in the underlying materials. This moisture seeks lower levels and may reach a point where all the spaces are completely filled with water. The water in this saturated zone is known as *ground water* and is the source of water for wells and springs. The upper limit of the zone is known as the *ground water table*. Between the ground water table and the surface is the moisture derived from rain and melted snow which is in the process of percolating downward and which is known as *vadose* or *soil water.*

The supply of underground water available in an area depends upon several factors: upon the amount of precipitation, upon the earth materials being of sufficient porosity to absorb large amounts of moisture, and upon the presence of large enough openings in the earth materials to give permeability or relatively free movement of the liquid. Subsurface formations which contain large quantities of water are called *aquifers.* The usefulness of such subsurface water depends not only upon its quantity but also upon the minerals that are dissolved in it. Waters charged with iron or sulphur often have an unpleasant taste and are not suitable for some industrial uses. Other waters contain quantities of calcium and magnesium which impart a characteristic called hardness, and some have qualities which are beneficial or harmful to the health of individuals who drink it.

Underground water is made available to man in many ways:

1. *Wells* or man-made openings that extend below the water table into the saturated zone are a major source of water in many

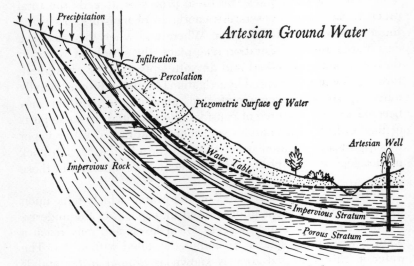

Fig. 40. Diagram showing the structures associated with the occurrence of an artesian well. The piezometric surface of water is an imaginary surface that coincides with points to which confined ground water will rise. (FROM Water, THE YEARBOOK OF AGRICULTURE, 1955, UNITED STATES DEPARTMENT OF AGRICULTURE.)

parts of the world. Many have been dug by hand and often are shallow and subject to pollution from surface waters or seepage. Since the ground water table may vary in depth or become lowered over a period of years, shallow wells frequently go dry. A more satisfactory source of water is found in deep wells that are drilled by modern equipment. The best are those which reach hundreds of feet below the surface into the lower portion of a well-supplied aquifer. The most satisfactory wells are those which have been located with respect to prior knowledge of the underlying rock structures.

2. *Artesian wells* are drilled or dug openings through which underground water flows to or very near the surface without pumping. Under certain conditions, sufficient pressure is built up so that when a well is drilled into an aquifer the water flows of its own accord. If artesian wells are to occur in an area the water-bearing formation must have the following characteristics: (*a*) it must consist of porous material such as sand or other loosely

consolidated particles which will permit free movement of the liquid, (*b*) it must be exposed at the surface in an area having sufficient precipitation to keep it supplied with water, (*c*) it must have considerable slope away from the area where it is exposed, and (*d*) it must lie between layers of impervious rock which prevent the water from escaping under pressure. (See Fig. 40.) Artesian structures are found in many parts of the world, both humid and arid, but they are most useful to man when they occur in dry regions. If many openings are drilled into artesian formations the pressure may drop and wells which formerly flowed of their own accord may require the installation of pumps.

3. *Springs* are found where ground water flows naturally at the surface. They may occur where a stream has cut its valley below the water table, or where water seeping downward through porous rocks encounters an impervious layer and moves horizontally along it, or where the waters of a wide area collect along a fault line and are forced to the surface by the influence of hot igneous materials at a lower level. In rural areas springs often are the only sources of drinking water, and in dry regions oasis settlements may develop around water sources of this type. Some areas with hot springs have become important as health resorts.

Surface Water. The moisture which falls to the earth's surface as precipitation and collects in streams as it flows toward oceans and seas is mankind's most important source of water. This accumulated precipitation, or *runoff*, provides most of the water used by cities. It is utilized by farmers for irrigation. It is the source of most of the water consumed by manufacturing industries or used for the generation of hydroelectric power, and it provides the routes for inland waterways. Lakes and reservoirs of various kinds may be regarded as runoff in storage. The great oceans and seas are repositories of runoff water from which winds pick up moisture and return it to the land.

The volume of surface water available in a given area varies according to the precipitation, temperature, vegetation cover, slope of the land, and nature of underlying earth materials. Although the amount of runoff is closely related to the annual precipitation, the value of the surface water also varies with differences in the type and seasonal distribution of precipitation. The cloudburst type of rainfall results in rapid runoff; streams are filled with water for short periods of time and carry only small amounts at other times. Where there are great seasonal fluctuations in precipitation, the full-flowing streams of one season may be dry watercourses during the rest of the year. Water-using activities must become adjusted to periods of short supply as well as to those when abundant quantities are available.

Stream flow represents the surface water which remains after precipitation has soaked into the ground, has evaporated into the atmosphere, and has served the needs of plants. The volume of water that accumulates in streams is reduced in areas having porous rock structures and high evaporation rates. A heavy vegetation cover has high moisture requirements of its own and also retards runoff. Streams which have a relatively uniform flow are of much greater use to man than those having great fluctuations, and streams in forested regions tend to have less fluctuation than those in areas with scanty vegetation cover.

Streams in humid regions may vary greatly in quantity of flow but all except the very small carry some water at all times. Fluctuations in flow reflect seasonal differences in precipitation and evaporation, changes in vegetation cover, the presence of snow and ice, or even differences in underground drainage. The occurrence of a winter season in which the precipitation accumulates in the form of ice or snow may result in retarded seasonal runoff which is followed by heavy flow, or even floods, in the higher temperatures of the warm season.

Streams in dry regions not only are generally smaller than those in humid areas but they vary greatly in the amount of water they carry and many are *intermittent,* or dry for part of the year. Deserts and many semiarid regions which do not have sufficient rainfall to support permanent streams may be crossed by rivers which have their headwaters in areas with heavy precipitation. These *exotic streams,* which often are the only important source of water in such dry areas, have characteristics typical of rivers in dry land regions, particularly a tendency toward seasonal flooding. Because of the scantiness of the vegetation cover, the hard-packed surface material, and the frequent lack of well-defined valleys in arid regions, broad areas may become inundated with surplus water after the infrequent periods of heavy rain. With their heavy loss of moisture by evaporation and seepage, rivers in dry regions gradually diminish in volume downstream. Accompanying this decline in volume is a corresponding decrease in the load of sediment that can be carried and an increase in the deposition of silt, mud, and sand. These accumulations are often of sufficient quantity to create sand bars and islands in a stream, causing it to divide into a number of channels or to become a *braided stream.*

The drainage features of various parts of the world display a number of *stream patterns.* Variations in the pattern are the result of differences in the slope of the land upon which the drainage system developed and differences in the resistance of the underlying rocks to erosion (see Chapter 5).

The most common drainage pattern, known as *dendritic,* consists of a tree-like arrangement made up of a main stream and successively smaller tributaries joining it at acute angles; it occurs in regions where the water flows over materials that have relatively similar resistance to erosion. If the stream flows over a regular succession of elongated zones of weak and resistant rocks such as is formed by folded or faulted structures, a *trellis* pattern develops. In this pattern the major streams are arranged in relatively straight parallel lines with tributaries joining at right angles. Single mountain peaks and other places which have a centrally located high area with drainageways extending out from it in all directions have *radial* patterns. *Irregular* drainage systems are characteristic of regions that have been covered by continental glaciation. The action of the moving ice tends to gouge out depressions in some places and deposit materials which dam up pre-existing drainage in others. Such areas have numerous lakes, ponds, and swamps through which streams wander in an aimless fashion as their waters seek lower elevation. The exotic rivers of dry regions have few tributaries and their courses frequently are interrupted by braided channels. Swiftly flowing streams will normally have straighter courses than those in which the water moves slowly.

WATER-CONSUMING ACTIVITIES

Some of the many ways that mankind utilizes water resources decrease the quantity and quality of the supply and some do not. Although the waters of the earth are never completely consumed, certain types of use tend to diminish local supplies and create periodic or widespread shortages of water.

Domestic and Industrial Water Supply. Because of the widespread increase in industrial activity and the corresponding growth of large urban centers, water supply for domestic purposes and for manufacturing is becoming critical in many parts of the world. The average daily use of water in the United States was estimated at 95 gallons per person in 1900, 138 gallons in 1950, and 143 gallons in 1955.[1] In an average American city, the per capita daily use is estimated to be 50 gallons for residential purposes, 50 gallons for industrial purposes, 10 gallons for public purposes, and 20 gallons for commercial purposes; and 10 gallons are lost in various ways. For more than half a century the daily consumer demand in American cities has been growing at the rate of one gallon per person annually. In a sense, these water demands are non-consumptive because an estimated 85 to 90 per cent of the water used in any city is discharged back into the surface supply. To reclaim this water, American communities have invested over 7,500 million dollars in public water works.

In addition to quantity requirements for water in urban centers, certain standards of quality must be met. It is important that public sources of water be free from disease-causing bacteria, from objectionable odors, from harmful minerals, and from excessive sediment.

During the period from 1939 to 1955 manufacturing industries in the United States increased their use of water by 36 per cent.[2] A Presidential Policy Commission forecast that the industrial use of water in the country would increase from the 80 billion gallons consumed per day in 1950 to 215 billion gallons per day in 1975. The largest percentage of the water used in manufacturing plants is for cooling purposes. In 1950 it was estimated that the average factory with an intake of more than 10 million gallons a day would utilize 54 per cent of the water for cooling, 32 per cent in processing, 9 per cent for boiler feed, 6 per cent for sanitation and cleaning, and 4 per cent for unclassified operations. This total

---

[1] *Water*, Yearbook of Agriculture, 1955 (U.S. Department of Agriculture [Washington, D.C., 1955]).

[2] *Ibid.*

exceeds 100 per cent because an estimated 5 per cent of the water intake is reused. The practice of reusing water is much more widespread than average figures in many industries indicate, and as industrial water needs expand in the future, the practice will undoubtedly be increased. Certain plants which have particularly heavy water requirements, such as those producing steel, synthetic rubber, pulp and paper, or chemicals, are usually located beside streams or lakes where a large supply is available.

Most of the water used by cities and industries comes from lakes and streams. On the basis of population, approximately 55 per cent of the persons served by community water systems in the United States receive their water from surface sources and a great many industrial establishments have their own intake systems. Rural users and small cities and towns depend more heavily upon ground water sources.

Irrigation. Of the total amount of water that has been diverted for use by man, a larger proportion is employed for the irrigation of crops than for any other purpose. In arid and semiarid lands water is the most important factor in the establishment of population centers, and few dry areas lacking a readily available source of water are utilized by man. Despite the problems associated with getting water on the land in such regions, irrigation agriculture is highly productive in terms of the investment of labor and capital per unit of area. Among the conditions which contribute to the high yields of desert oases are the unleached nature and high mineral content of dry-land soils, the relative freedom from insect pests and weeds, the high percentage of sunshine, and the fact that water can be applied in the proper amounts when it is needed.

Although water from almost all sources is utilized for irrigation, surface runoff is the most important. Since there is a large moisture loss through evaporation and drainage, the precipitation runoff of a large area is often required to irrigate a relatively small amount of farm land. From the time man first began to live in fixed settlements and to cultivate crops, he has devised many different methods for maintaining a supply of water on dry lands. Ancient Egyptians and other peoples of the Near East diverted the flood waters of rivers into basins where sufficient quantities of water to produce a crop could be absorbed by the soil. This *basin flooding* has an advantage over many other types of irrigation because the silt present in flood waters is dropped on the fields and helps maintain the fertility of the soil. Other ancient peoples of Asia and Africa constructed elaborate systems of underground tunnels (*kanats, qanats, foggaras*) leading from places with abundant water, usually at the head of alluvial fans, to adjacent lowland areas. Wells, either dug or artesian types, have long been used as sources of irrigation water. Various devices such as well sweeps, water wheels, windlasses, screw lifts, and now mechanical pumps have been utilized to elevate the water from non-flowing aquifers.

In modern large-scale irrigation, dams are constructed across major streams to impound the flow into large storage reservoirs, and diversion canals carry the water to the areas where it is to be utilized. In some cases water is applied to the land by a system of small canals and ditches; in others, elaborate overhead sprinkler arrangements have been constructed. One of the major problems of modern irrigation agriculture is that of maintaining soil fertility. The life-giving silt—which would be deposited in fields subjected to the ancient technique of basin flooding—under modern methods has been dropped elsewhere, usually behind the giant dams. In addition, because of excessive evaporation, mineral salts held in solution in irrigation water may accumulate in quantities sufficient to ruin the soil for crops.

It should be noted that not all irrigation is restricted to regions with low precipitation. For example, peoples in many parts of the Far East have long been dependent upon paddy rice for a major portion of their food supply. The amount of land in humid areas associated with this wet-field rice production may be greater than that of all areas under irrigation in dry regions. In humid parts of the United States and Europe there has been a recent increase in the amount of land put under irrigation to supplement precipitation during the growing season. This practice usually results in substantial increases in crop yields and is generally limited to high value crops such as fruit and vegetables.

NON-CONSUMING WATER USES

Water that is used for routes of transportation, to produce electricity, or for recreational purposes is not diminished in quantity and can be used over and over again—therefore these are non-consuming uses. However, water is not a free resource for these purposes because its utilization requires considerable investment in capital, human energy, management, and technology.

Water Power. One of the first steps in the development of modern civilization was taken when man learned to construct water wheels as a source of power. Man's utilization of the weight of falling water for energy freed him from dependence upon his own or animal strength for the performance of many tasks. Large wheels placed adjacent to falls or rapids or beside streams harnessed the momentum of diverted water falling upon cups or paddles to provide power for grinding flour, sawing timber, or operating simple machines. This direct use of water power tied mills and settlements to stream-side locations, and small or medium-sized rivers were more desired than large ones because they could be utilized more easily. At many sites, dams were constructed to provide the necessary fall of water or to equalize the flow.

Dependence upon direct water power declined after the use of the steam-powered engine became widespread, but mills and settlements continued to be situated near streams because of the need for large quantities of water to produce this form of energy. Since the development of hydroelectric generators, the force of falling water can be transformed into electrical energy which is utilized to produce heat, light, and mechanical motion. Today electrical power is widely consumed over the settled parts of the world but it cannot be economically transmitted by wire more than 250 to 300 miles from where it is generated. Because of this and other factors, electricity generated by large steam plants is often cheaper than that derived from water power, and it is estimated that the amount of electricity generated by steam in the United States is twice that originating from hydro-power sources. However, since coal and oil, which provide the power for the generation of thermal electricity, are exhaustible resources and water power is a renewable resource, this situation may change in the future.

The ideal physical condition for the production of hydroelectric power involves a large stream with a swift and steady flow. If the stream flow is irregular, it may not be economical to construct a power plant capable of utilizing maximum flow, and the investment required for installations which harness the minimum flow may be unprofitable. Regions with the best water power resources are those which have abundant precipitation and sufficient slope to permit maximum utilization of the weight of falling water. Areas having many swamps and lakes to provide natural storage reservoirs can utilize maximum water power potential at minimum cost by means of dams. The large dams which are frequently associated with important power installations function to regularize the flow of water by creating artificial lakes and to create a situation where a large volume of water may be induced to drop a great distance. For the construction of power dams, the best sites are those which (1) have a narrows in resistant rock so that the dam can be constructed economically, (2) have an area upstream from the dam site which can function as a storage basin, and (3) are relatively near large markets for electrical power.

Water Transportation. Since ancient times the waters of rivers, lakes, and seas have served man as important routes of transportation. Although the development of land and air methods of travel has provided faster and more efficient means of transportation, water routes are still the cheapest means of moving many commodities.

The major advantages of water transportation are that the route itself is provided without cost and large or bulky cargoes can be carried more cheaply by ship than by railroads, trucks, or airplanes. Although channels often need to be deepened or straightened, and canals are sometimes necessary to connect natural waterways, the costs of establishing and maintaining these waterways may often be much less than for alternate land routes. Water carriers have an advantage for moving bulky goods because they can be constructed with larger capacities at lower investment per unit of space without correspondingly greater expense of operation. This is particularly true where the length of haul is great and where loading and unloading effort can be kept at a minimum.

The disadvantages of water transportation are essentially those of location and physical character of the route. The direction of flow of a major river or the arrangement of a chain of connected lakes may not be appropriate to best serve the demands of commerce. If the major trade routes of a country like the United States are east-west and the trend of a large river like the Mississippi is north-south, the river will not be as satisfactory a transportation route as if it flowed east-west. Rivers often have other characteristics which detract from their usefulness as routes of trade. If a river has a very meandering course, cargo carriers must move slowly and travel excessive distances; variations in flow may mean flooded conditions in one season and insufficient water depth for navigation in another; and shifts in channels may make it difficult to establish reliable routes. Expensive locks or canals have to be built around rapids and waterfalls, and some streams lack satisfactory landing places. Rivers in the middle and high latitudes may be ice-bound for several months each winter and be closed to navigation. Despite the improvements that have been made in river vessels and ocean carriers, the movement of commerce by water is much slower than by land or air.

Water for Recreation. As more people have more leisure time, water resources are gaining importance as centers of recreational activity. Many lakes, streams, waterfalls, beaches, and other water features have long been valued for their scenic beauty, and increasingly larger numbers of people visit areas which have facilities for swimming, boating, sailing, and fishing. Although mountains and forests are valuable physical assets, probably the water resources are the most important natural attributes of areas that attract large numbers of vacationers, tourists, and weekend visitors. While the automobile has greatly increased the mobility of persons seeking to enjoy their leisure time in water-oriented recreational activities, the most popular resorts and playgrounds are those which are readily accessible to large population centers. Areas with superior attractions are often so far from major urban centers that the time and money involved in travel limits the number of people able to enjoy them.

MULTIPLE USE WATER PROJECTS

There are so many ways that water resources can be made beneficial to mankind that the various uses which may be desired in an area are often in conflict with each other. The diversion of water from a stream for irrigation or domestic purposes will detract from its utility for navigation or hydroelectric power, the use of the waters of a river for sewage disposal by a community or manufacturing plant will impair its value downstream as a source of water or for recreational activity, and the construction of dams to control floods may result in the permanent inundation of some of the best farm lands along a valley or may limit the value of the stream for navigation. Since there are so many ways to utilize the waters of an area, and numerous controversies may develop from conflicting demands, multiple-use water projects have been established to place the control of a river system or drainage basin under a single authority.

The first large scale river basin development project was established in the valley of the Tennessee in the United States. It was put into operation in 1933 after several disastrous floods had occurred and because of the depressed economic conditions in the area. Because the waters of the Tennessee cross or touch the boundaries of five states, and drain the waters of several others, management of the project was placed under an agency of the national government known as the Tennessee Valley Authority (T.V.A.). The project involved the construction of large dams along the river and its major tributaries for the purpose of controlling floods, producing hydroelectric power, and improving navigation.

As the program developed, the T.V.A. became involved in numerous activities that were not directly related to water control. Persons living in areas that would be flooded after dams were built had to be moved elsewhere, making it necessary for the authority to participate in resettlement and housing projects. Since the waters behind the dams would become subject to siltation and in time could be rendered useless for the storage of water by the accumulations of sediment, efforts were made to reduce the amount of solid material in the waters that would be impounded. Thus programs of soil conservation, afforestation, and watershed rehabilitation were instituted. These activities and the need for the resettlement of many families resulted in the institution of a program to survey the land capabilities and existing land use of the entire basin.

The T.V.A. includes a series of thirty-one multipurpose dams, twenty of which were built by the T.V.A., six are privately owned but controlled by the authority, four were secured from a utility company, and one was built by the government at an earlier date. Nine of the structures are *long dams* designed mainly to facilitate navigation on the Tennessee River, and the remaining *high dams,* on major tributaries, are primarily for flood control and power production. The long dams have created a series of narrow lakes which form a 9-foot deep navigation channel some 630 miles long from Paducah, Kentucky, to Knoxville, Tennessee. The high dams, together with steam-generated power plants controlled by the T.V.A., sell over 56,000,000,000 kilowatt hours of electricity each year. T.V.A. dams with a storage capacity of some 12,000,000 acre feet impound potential flood waters, which can be released during periods of drought, and substantially reduce the dangers from floods along the Tennessee, Ohio, and Mississippi rivers. Among the other accomplishments of the T.V.A. have been the reforestation of over 200,000 acres of cut-over or marginal land, the reclamation of thousands of acres of damaged crop land, a substantial increase in the industrial capacity in the area, and the creation of recreational attractions which draw thousands of visitors each year.

In spite of the original objections to the socialistic nature of the program, the numerous lawsuits, the heavy financial investment, and other problems, the T.V.A. is considered to have been a successful undertaking. Most of the original objectives have been met and the standards of living in the area have been considerably improved. Similar projects, many with somewhat different scope and objectives, have been established by state and national governments, not only in the United States but in other parts of the world. The one thing they have in common is the concept that multiple-use management is vital to the efficient utilization of the water resources of river basins. Other notable projects of this type have been established in the Central Valley of California and the Missouri Valley in the United States, the Cauca Valley of Colombia, the São Francisco Valley of Brazil, the Rhone Valley of France, and the Murray-Darling Basin of Australia.

LEGAL ASPECTS OF WATER RESOURCE USE

The conflicting interests of water users in an area have frequently resulted in litigation involving both individuals and governmental units. Laws controlling the utilization of water resources have characterized legal systems from ancient times to the present. The doctrines that governments in humid regions have developed regarding water rights are quite different from those that have evolved in arid lands. Legal codes to resolve questions over the use of water fall under three general headings:

1. The principle of *riparian rights* evolved in Western Europe where the most important demands for water were for navigation and power. It is based upon the concept that river-bank users may divert water from a stream provided that it is returned to the channel undiminished in quantity and unaltered in quality.

2. The doctrine of *priority or appropriated rights* developed in regions where water for irrigation and hydraulic mining was a primary consideration. This code is based upon the principle that the rights of first users take precedence over those who arrive later. It safeguards the interests of those having investments depending upon water availability. Under the priority rights doctrine the first person to put the waters of a stream to beneficial use cannot have his supply jeopardized by a new user. His right to divert ends, however, when the use ceases.

3. The principle of *equable distribution* is a more recent type of code, a compromise plan, which has evolved in areas where the total claims for water exceed the available supply. It represents an attempt to bring water legislation into harmony with the needs and resources of the time.

Almost all water laws are subject to a variety of interpretations, and litigation over water resources has entered the courts at all levels. Individual farmers and local governments often take legal action concerning the right to remove waters from a stream for domestic uses or for irrigation. Cities and manufacturing concerns have resorted to the courts over questions of water pollution caused by the dumping of waste materials into streams and over conflicts arising from excessive quantities of water being diverted for domestic and industrial purposes. Examples of legal action reaching the state level are found in the disagreements among Nevada, Arizona, and California over the waters of the Colorado River and in the disputes over the right of the city of Chicago to divert water from Lake Michigan. At the international level some of the most famous controversies between the United

States and Mexico have been based upon the proper allocation of the waters of the lower Colorado River and of the lower Rio Grande.

SUPPLEMENTARY READING

Bennison, Ernest W. *Ground Water: Its Development, Uses, and Conservation.* St. Paul: E. E. Johnson, Inc., 1947.

Forman, J., and Fink, O. E. (eds.). *Water and Man: A Study in Ecology.* Columbus: Friends of the Land, 1950.

Frank, Bernard, and Netboy, Anthony. *Water, Land, and People.* New York: Alfred A. Knopf, Inc., 1950.

King, Thomson. *Water, Miracle of Nature.* New York: Macmillan Co., 1953.

Kuenen, P. H. *Realms of Water.* New York: John Wiley & Sons, Inc., Science Editions, 1963.

Leopold, Luna B., and Maddock, T. *The Flood Control Controversy.* New York: Ronald Press, Inc., 1954.

Linsley, Ray K.; Kohler, M. A.; and Paulhus, J. L. H. *Applied Hydrology.* New York: McGraw-Hill Book Co., Inc., 1949.

Water. The Yearbook of Agriculture, 1955, U.S. Department of Agriculture. Washington, D.C.: Government Printing Office, 1955.

10

The Oceans and Seas

In terms of the area covered, the earth's oceanic waters are more important than any other feature of the natural environment except climate. The fact that a relatively small portion of this book is devoted to the maritime surface of the earth may at first seem inappropriate, but the reader is reminded that most of the drama of man's activities is played upon the great land masses.

The importance of the oceans has been mentioned in earlier chapters. They have a profound influence upon the temperature and precipitation of adjacent land masses and are an important factor in climatic variations, which in turn cause differences in natural vegetation and soils. The great seas of the world are the primary storehouse which maintains the hydrologic cycle, and the precipitation which stems indirectly from this source is a major factor in erosion. In their somewhat closer relations to mankind, the oceans are an important source of food and of useful minerals. At times large water bodies have served as barriers to the movement of population groups; in other cases, they have facilitated the transportation of goods and people. In addition to the many benefits man receives from them, it is somewhat paradoxical that the oceans serve as a major attraction for recreational activities on one hand and as the dumping place for refuse on the other.

THE WORLD OCEAN

How many oceans are there on the planet earth: one, four, five, or seven? The interconnected body of water which extends over more than 70 per cent of the earth's surface may be referred to as the *world ocean* and each of its major subdivisions lying between continents is known as an *ocean*. The term *sea* may be used to designate the continuous salt waters that cover a large part of the earth, and many partially land-enclosed subdivisions of the oceans are also known as seas.

The total area of the world ocean is over 142 million square miles. Although some authorities disagree, geographers generally consider that there are five separate oceans. They are (with the approximate area of each in million square miles) as follows: Arctic 5.4, Atlantic 28.7, Pacific 64.0, Indian 28.4, and Antarctic 12.5. Some scientists believe that the Antarctic is not a separate ocean at all but merely the southern parts of three oceans surrounding a land mass having the same name. Others contend that the Arctic is really a "polar sea" which is part of the Atlantic Ocean. The Pacific, sometimes termed the *water hemisphere*, is larger than all of the earth's land masses combined.

The total volume of the water in the oceans is estimated to be more than 328 million cubic miles. If all the irregularities were removed from the solid outer crust of the earth, the maritime waters would cover it to a depth in excess of two miles.

OCEANIC WATERS

The great volume of water which is found between the floor of the sea and the bottom of the atmosphere has numerous physical and chemical properties which cause it to differ considerably from one part of the world to another.

Chemical Composition. The waters of the sea are made up of dilute solutions of a number of salts. The salinity of these waters is usually expressed by the ratio of parts of salts present per thousand parts of water. Salinity varies from 33 to 37 parts per thousand, with the average for all oceans being about 35. Of this total, approximately 27 parts are sodium chloride, 3.75 parts magnesium chloride, 1.65 parts magnesium sulphate, and 1.3 parts calcium sulphate.[1] More than trace quantities of over 40 other chemical elements are found in solution in oceanic waters. In addition to dissolved solids, sea water carries in solution most of the gases found in the atmosphere, though not in the same

---

[1] Authority for quantitative statements contained in this chapter is N. Bowditch, *American Practical Navigator* (U.S. Navy Hydrographic Office Publication No. 9 [Washington, D.C., 1962]).

proportions. Some elements, such as chlorine, bromine, sulphur, and boron, are more abundant in the ocean than they are on land. Other elements such as silicon, nitrogen, and phosphorus are important for the growth of living organisms in ocean waters. Man has learned to extract magnesium, bromine, and other minerals from the sea, as well as common salt (sodium chloride).

The composition of sea water varies from one place to another and at different depths in a particular locality. Salinity is generally highest in the subtropics, lower in the equatorial regions, and lowest in the polar areas. Restricted seas in humid regions, such as the Baltic, have low salinity because fresh water from in-flowing rivers dilutes the sea water. Similar seas in arid parts of the world have high surface evaporation and high salt content. The waters of the great ocean depths have lower salinity than those at the surface.

Temperature. Temperatures in the world ocean vary widely with both locality and depth. Maximum values range from approximately 90° F. in the Persian Gulf in summer to 28° F. (the usual minimum freezing point of sea water) in the polar regions. Because colder water is denser it tends to sink below warmer water, and therefore the sea everywhere shows a decrease in temperature with depth.

Pressure. Pressure affects all physical properties of sea water to some extent but its influence is not as great as that of salinity or temperature. Pressure is measured in terms of pounds per square inch. At a depth of 1,000 feet, the average pressure is 445 pounds per square inch; at 2,000 feet it is 892 pounds; at 4,000 feet it is 1,788 pounds; and at 6,000 feet it is 2,685 pounds. The increase in pressure with depth is almost constant because water is only slightly compressible.

Color. The color of sea water varies considerably. Shades of blue are prevalent because of the scattering of sunlight by minute particles suspended in the water. Blue light is of short wave length and is more effectively scattered than are longer wave lengths of light. The greens which are often predominant in shallow seas are a mixture of blue, which is the result of scattering of sunlight, with soluble yellow pigments associated with microscopic floating plants. Brownish or reddish brown waters receive their color when certain types of algae are present in large quantities.

Other physical properties of oceanic waters such as density, compressibility, viscosity, and conductivity are of great importance in many fields of study, but discussion of them here seems unnecessary for the purposes of this book.

LIFE IN THE OCEANS

Sea water contains all the chemical elements necessary to support plant and animal life, and organic material is present in large quantities. Marine life may be classified in three main groups: *plankton* (tiny floating plants or feebly swimming or floating animals), *nekton* (strong swimming animals such as fish), and *benthos* (plants and animals living on the ocean bottom, such as seaweed, barnacles, and crabs).

Plankton. Plankton vary in size from microscopic particles to lengths of a fraction of an inch. Microscopic floating plants are referred to as *phytoplankton* and feebly swimming or floating animals are known as *zooplankton*. Directly or indirectly, nearly all marine life depends upon these organisms, which are carried by ocean currents because they do not have the strength to choose their own environment. By the process of photosynthesis [2] phytoplankton change chemical nutrients of the sea into primary foods which are utilized by zooplankton and some larger forms of life. The larger sea animals feed upon zooplankton and upon each other. The excretion of animals and the bacterial action accompanying the decomposition of dead plants and animals replace the chemical nutrients used by phytoplankton. So it is that there is a food cycle in continuous operation, from chemical nutrient to phytoplankton, to zooplankton, to nekton and benthos, and back to chemical nutrient.

The scarcity or abundance of marine life in a locality is related to the supply of phytoplankton, which require sunlight and chemical nutrients. Sunlight of sufficient strength to allow photosynthesis penetrates the ocean waters down to depths of 500 feet; within this zone photosynthesis will be restricted mainly by the supply of chemical nutrients. Where the water is shallow, these nutrients are churned up from the ocean bottom by the motion of

---

[2] Photosynthesis is the process by which green plants utilize the energy of sunlight absorbed by chlorophyll to produce carbohydrate food.

the water and are carried into the upper sunlight zone. For this reason many shallow places in the sea, such as the Grand Banks, which have a concentration of plankton to support larger marine animals, are good fishing grounds. Similarly, in polar areas chemical nutrients are abundant because they are brought upward by the convective currents that are set up as cold surface water subsides and is replaced by warmer water from the depths. Conversely, in the tropics the ocean water is relatively stable and chemical nutrients tend to sink below the zone where sunlight can penetrate.

Nekton. It has long been accepted that fish, shellfish, and sea mammals will be found in greatest numbers in areas where there are concentrations of plant plankton. Since the major commercial fishing grounds of the world are generally located outside of the tropics, in the northern hemisphere, the statement has been made that there are smaller numbers of edible fish in tropical waters because there is less plankton present. It is quite probable that the marine life of tropical waters is as abundant as it is in cooler areas, but that like terrestrial plant life in tropical climates (Chapter 7) the number of species present is unusually large and there are few local concentrations of species. The facts that in tropical oceanic waters the fish do not run in schools and that their flesh has greater susceptibility to spoilage after being caught may be just as important as plankton supply in explaining the underdeveloped nature of commercial fishing in tropical seas. Whatever the case, the animal life of the oceans does have great complexity of form and structure. A multitude of different habitats are available and many marine animals, like animals on land, have a great range of mobility. The distribution of the various types of nekton is as complex as that of land-based fauna. Each species has its preferred habitat but most have some degree of adaptability, and distinct regional patterns are rather difficult to define.

Benthos. The types of marine life that grow on the ocean floor depend upon the nature of the sea bottom and the amount of exposure to wave action. Sandy shores and wave-swept rocky coasts usually have sparse populations but protected bays and inlets may be teeming with life. Where rocky shores occur adjacent to protected waters the shore zone and bottom may abound with seaweed, barnacles, and mussels, and a variety of crabs, worms, and other mobile forms. The larger plant life such as kelp, rockweed, and other types of algae are among the simplest in the plant world. Relatively shallow waters near coastlines receive organic matter from inland areas and are particularly rich in animal life. At ocean depths greater than 1,000 feet, where perpetual darkness prevails, life on the ocean floor is dependent upon small amounts of food that filter down from the upper lighted zone and tends to be small and inconspicuous.

THE MOVEMENT OF OCEAN WATER

The waters of the sea appear to be always in motion. Some movements are small and of irregular occurrence, some are periodic and limited to certain areas, and others affect entire ocean basins. All represent an attempt by nature to maintain equilibrium in a liquid mass.

Waves. Most undulations on the surface of the sea, or *waves*, are caused by wind, but some result from tidal activity, submarine earthquakes, or volcanic eruptions. When a light breeze begins to blow across smooth water, small wavelets form. If the breeze subsides these ripples disappear, but if the wind velocity increases, larger *gravity waves* develop and progress with the wind. The water in a wave does not move greatly; the motion is that of the wave impulse. Waves are not particularly deflected by earth rotation but move in the direction in which the wind is blowing. As the wind ceases or its speed diminishes, the resulting decrease in friction and spreading reduces the height of the waves as the waves move across the surface of the water. This reduction occurs slowly and the swell continues until some obstruction, such as a coastline, is reached. The effects of waves upon the landforms of shorelines are discussed in Chapter 5.

The highest parts of waves are called *crests* and the intervening depressions *troughs*. *Wave length* is the horizontal distance between successive crests; *wave height* is the vertical distance between trough and crest.

Tides. Tides are the periodic motions of oceanic waters caused by variations in the gravitational attraction of the moon and the sun upon different parts of the earth as the earth rotates upon its axis. The rise and fall of the tide is accompanied by a horizontal movement of water known as the *tidal current*, which floods and ebbs.

Gravity emanating from the center of the earth tends to hold the planet in the shape of a sphere. The moon and the sun are disturbing forces. In their relationship with each other, the moon and the earth revolve about a common center of mass. Gravitational attraction holds them together and an equal, but opposing, centrifugal force keeps them apart. On the half of the earth facing the moon, water from the fluid ocean is drawn toward the moon's gravitational attraction; in the hemisphere opposite the moon the water level of the oceans is raised by the action of centrifugal force. These tide-producing forces build up high tides on the parts of the earth nearest to and farthest from the moon, leaving a low tide belt between them. As the earth rotates, every point on its surface passes through two high and two low tide areas each day.

The sun acts upon the waters of the earth in a manner similar to the moon, but the sun is so much farther away from earth than the moon that its effect is considerably less and sun tides generally appear to be modifications of the lunar tides. When the earth, moon, and sun are nearly in line (during the times of new and full moon) so that lunar and solar tides coincide, high tides are unusually high and the intervening low tides are unusually low. This situation occurs every two weeks and is known as the period of the *spring tide*.[3] When the line of the earth and sun is at right angles to that of the earth and moon (when the moon is at its first and third quarters), the sun tides detract from the lunar tides, causing the variation between the level of high tide and low tide to be much less. This is the period of the *neap tide* and also occurs every two weeks.

Although the tide-producing forces are distributed uniformly over the earth, the interference of land masses and the differences in size and shape of ocean basins keep the ocean tides from developing in a simple and regular pattern. Each ocean basin, and its adjacent seas, has its own response to tidal forces. The tidal range of nearly enclosed bodies of water such as the Mediterranean Sea is usually slight, but on exposed seacoasts the tides

---

[3] This term has nothing to do with the season of the year.

will average between 5 and 10 feet. Estuaries often have great differences between high and low tides; the incoming bulge of water becomes constricted into increasingly narrower confines, forming a very high tide, and when the tidal current moves out again, the water from the narrow upper portion is spread out over an increasingly broader area in a very low tide.

Ocean Currents. In addition to wave movements and tides, the motion of the oceanic waters is influenced by a great circulatory system made up of a number of giant eddies or whirls. The general pattern of these ocean currents and their importance as climatic controls has been described in Chapter 3. A more detailed picture of the circulatory system is shown in Figure 41, page 172.

Geographers generally agree that winds are the primary generating force for the creation of ocean currents. The relationship between ocean currents and the general circulation of the atmosphere can be seen by comparing Figure 41 with Figure 17 (page 36). Density differences in oceanic waters are an important secondary factor, and depth of water, subsurface topography, extent and location of land masses, and the deflective force of earth rotation, all affect the movement of ocean waters. The rate of movement within the circulatory system varies from as much as six miles per hour to an almost imperceptible drift. The speed of flow is more rapid at the surface than it is along the ocean bottom. Over a period of several hundred years, probably every drop of water in the world's oceans has moved from tropical to polar seas and from the ocean floor to the surface several times.

If the Atlantic and Pacific Oceans are considered as divided into northern and southern parts, there are seven principal oceans on the earth, each with its own virtually closed circulatory system (see Fig. 41). Waters in the Antarctic Ocean move eastward around the polar land mass. Water from the Atlantic enters the Arctic Ocean between Iceland and Norway, advances around the North Pole in a counterclockwise fashion, and emerges along the eastern coast of Greenland. In the other great whirls, water drifts around the ocean basins in a clockwise direction in the northern hemisphere and in a counterclockwise manner in the southern hemisphere. Except where the eastern bulge of South America forces water moving westward from central Africa to

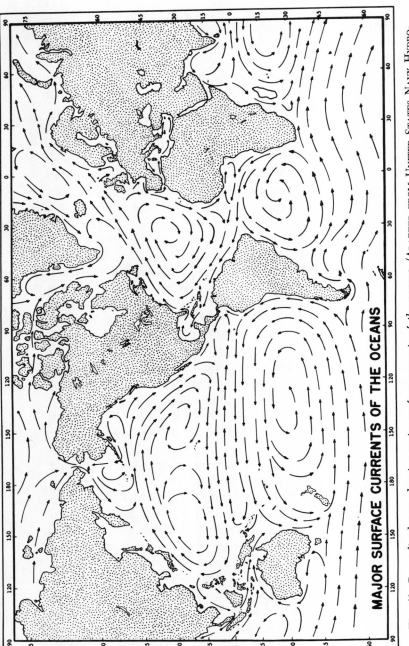

MAJOR SURFACE CURRENTS OF THE OCEANS

Fig. 41. Generalized map showing major surface currents of the oceans. (ADAPTED FROM UNITED STATES NAVY HYDRO-
GRAPHIC OFFICE PUBLICATION No. 9. BASE MAP IS A MERCATOR PROJECTION PLOTTED BY IBM 7090 COMPUTER, AT THE
UNIVERSITY OF MICHIGAN COMPUTING CENTER, FROM A PROGRAM PREPARED BY W. R. TOBLER.)

veer toward the north, large quantities of water in this great circulatory system do not cross the equator.

THE OCEAN FLOOR

Although knowledge about the features of the ocean floor is still incomplete, much progress has been made in recent years. Using ships equipped with echo-sounding devices, and with concentrated efforts in connection with the 1957-1959 International Geophysical Year, scientists have learned the answers to many of the mysteries of the ocean depths. Some of the processes and forms of the sea bottom are similar to those on land surfaces and others are quite different, but the variety of features under the sea is just as great as on land. There are rugged mountains, wide plains, and deep valleys that sometimes surpass the features of the continents in size and extent.

The Continental Shelf. The great land masses of the earth are bordered by terrace-like surfaces which extend as far as 600 miles out under the sea and are known as the *continental shelf.* The continental shelf is a relatively smooth surface that slopes gently seaward to depths of approximately 600 feet. It is often absent along mountainous coasts and is widest where broad plains border the sea. At the outer edge of the continental shelf the *continental slope* descends sharply to the great ocean depths.

The shallow water zones around the margins of the ocean basins are in many ways submerged parts of the continental land masses. The underwater topography includes some depressions and ridges, the tops of which may rise above the water level as islands, but an outstanding feature is the large number of deep submarine canyons that stretch out from the coastline. Many, but not all, of these gorges extend seaward from the mouths of major rivers, giving evidence that they were once the valleys of continental streams. It is probable that much of the continental shelf was dry land in a past geologic period.

Submarine Mountains. It is now known that there are mountain ranges under the sea that compare with those of the continents in height and extent. Although they are found in mid-ocean locations, their arrangement roughly parallels the margins of the major land masses, and they divide the oceans into a number of basins. The best known of these submerged mountain ranges is the Mid-Atlantic Ridge which extends through the middle part of the Atlantic from Iceland almost to Antarctica. It is approximately 1,000 miles in width and rises from 5,000 to 10,000 feet above the floor of nearby basins. In a few places it approaches the surface and a number of small islands such as the Azores, Ascension, and Tristan da Cunha represent the tops of its highest peaks. Ridges of similar proportions extend across the Pacific in a northwest to southeast alignment, and southward from India through the Indian Ocean.

In addition to the massive submerged cordilleras, the ocean depths also contain hundreds of isolated, steep-sided peaks called *sea mounts,* which rise several hundred feet above their base. Many, if not most, of these are thought to be volcanic peaks that have remained uneroded in the quiet waters of the ocean depths. The coral islands of the Pacific such as the Gilberts, Marshalls, and Tuamotus are sea mounts with coral growth on top of them. Sea mounts are seldom found on the continental shelf; they are most numerous on the seaward sides of the great ocean trenches.

Submarine mountains and sea mounts are produced by the same tectonic forces that caused the development of ranges and peaks on the continents. They have not been subjected to most of the forces of erosion that wear down uplands in terrestrial mountainous areas and retain many of the characteristics that were produced by vulcanism and diastrophism.

Oceanic Trenches. The greatest depths in the ocean occur in narrow and elongated trenches which are found near the margins of continents. The bottom of one, the Marianas Trench, is more than 35,000 feet below the ocean surface and several others are farther below sea level than the highest mountains on land are above it. Many are much larger than corresponding depressions or basins on land. These features were formed by diastrophism and they are situated in areas of frequent earthquake and volcanic activity. Many of these giant submarine canyons are located close to chains of islands such as the Aleutians and the Kurils, or along the outside arcs of such large clusters of islands as the East and West Indies.

Ocean Plains. Other than the relatively level continental shelf, plains are not as common under the sea as they are on land masses. Deposition, which helps to even out irregularities on the continents, is very slow away from the margins of the great land masses; the usual processes of erosion are generally absent and the features resulting from earth movement and vulcanism are preserved for long periods of time. Broad stretches of relatively level sea bottom are found on the flanks of the Mid-Atlantic Ridge (particularly east of Bermuda), in the Indian Ocean southeast of Ceylon, and at scattered places in the Pacific Basin.

ISLANDS IN THE SEA

As previously mentioned, the tops of high features rising from the ocean floor frequently emerge above the level of the sea as islands. These parcels of dry land may reach almost continental proportions in size, or may have an area of only a few acres. An extended line of islands is referred to as an *island chain;* a cluster of islands is called an *archipelago.* Islands are classified as either *continental* or *oceanic.*

Continental Islands. Most of the large islands of the world (such as Greenland, Borneo, Sumatra, New Guinea, and Tasmania) have close geologic connections with a nearby continent. They are unsubmerged parts of the continental shelf and are separated from the larger land mass by narrow and shallow waters. In past geologic time, as warping of the earth's crust caused changes in the relative levels of the land and the sea, these islands were connected to the continent by *land bridges.* For this reason their flora and fauna, as well as their rock structure, are similar to those of the adjacent mainland.

Oceanic Islands. Islands in mid-ocean, remote from the continents, are the crests of sea mounts or submarine mountains and most of them in one way or another are of volcanic origin. Some are mountainous with rugged volcanic peaks, and are called *high islands;* others are built up by coral formations, have little relief, and are known as *low islands.*

The high islands are built up from the ocean floor as enormous piles of lava accumulate until the crests of the mountains protrude above the surface of the water. Many of these volcanoes are still active and have frequent earthquake tremors. As was pointed out earlier, chains of these volcanic islands are arranged in arcs near the borders of some deep oceanic trenches.

Low islands are formed by accumulations of the skeletal remains of small sea animals called *corals* which grow in warm,
shallow, and silt-free water. These shell-forming and lime-secret-
ing marine forms may cause the development of limestone structures of considerable extent. Coral accumulations sometimes construct *fringing reefs* along the coasts of continents, continental
islands, or high islands. However, when they occur in mid-ocean
they may form low islands by building up the crests of submerged volcanoes or other types of sea mounts. In some places
where coral reefs have developed on the flanks of volcanic islands
in mid-ocean, subsidence has taken place and the volcanoes have
become submerged, leaving circular chains of low islands surrounding shallow lagoons. Such features are called *atolls*.

THE MARGINS OF THE OCEANS

The zone of contact between the continents and the oceans is
an area of constant change and many different processes take
place. Deposition by waters flowing from the streams of the land
meets with the erosive action of oceanic waves and currents.
Diastrophic events, changes in the level of the land and the sea,
and the accumulation of biological material, all have an influence
upon the appearance of coastlines. Although most shorelines are
extremely varied, four general types are usually recognized.

Shorelines of Emergence. Where the margins of a continental
land mass are slowly rising, or the level of the sea is subsiding,
the ocean waters come in contact with land that has recently
been a part of the sea bottom. As the land emerges, a new coastline is formed seaward of the old one and a portion of the continental shelf becomes exposed as a coastal plain. Because the surface of much of the continental shelf is quite level, the new
shoreline tends to be regular in outline and the land behind it flat
and poorly drained. Since the waters near the land are shallow,
approaching waves do not reach the shore but break some distance from the coast and deposit materials which eventually form
long sandbars paralleling the shoreline. These offshore bars become separated from the mainland by the shallow quiet waters of
lagoons. Usually there are breaks in the offshore bars which allow
tidal currents to enter and to bring in sand which is added to the
sediments deposited by streams from the continent. These de-

posits, plus erosion on the seaward side, cause the bars to move slowly landward. In time, as vegetation grows around the margins of the lagoon, the bars may become part of the main shoreline. Shorelines of emergence, then, have few irregularities, are backed by flat terrain with sluggish streams flowing across it, and display numerous offshore bars and lagoons on their seaward margins. Because the waters offshore are shallow and there are few indentations to provide protected anchorages for ships, this type of coast is not conducive to the development of large seaports. The western coast of the Gulf of Mexico, the southern coast of Argentina, and the coasts of northern Chile and Peru have emergent shorelines.

Shorelines of Submergence. Where the level of the land is slowly subsiding, or sea level is rising, the surface of the ocean is encroaching upon the land and parts of the continent are becoming part of the sea bottom. If the submerged land is a level plain the sea will advance far up river valleys, inundating lowlands and permitting tidal currents to back up rivers for some distance upstream. The mouths of the streams become drowned, forming broad shallow indentations of the sea called *estuaries*. The eastern coast of Great Britain, the southeastern coast of New England, and the southern Baltic coast are all examples of shorelines of submergence which have developed seaward from plains.

If submergence takes place along hilly or mountainous coasts the drowned river valleys have deeper water, the inward advance of oceanic waters may be greater, and the interstream areas form bold peninsulas and rugged offshore islands. The sunken valleys, which are known as *rias*, are characteristic of the coasts of Greece, northwestern Spain, Brittany, and Maine. The rias usually provide good anchorages for ships but the rugged nature of the adjacent terrain and the prevalence of thin soils frequently preclude the development of large seaport cities.

Where the submergence of mountainous coasts has been accompanied, or preceded, by valley glaciation, *fjorded coasts* such as are found in Norway, western Canada, southern Chile, and New Zealand are characteristic. Such coastlines represent the drowning of valleys that were carved by glacial erosion. The fjords are long, narrow, deep, and steep-sided landward encroachments of the sea. There is little level land except possibly at the head of the fjords, but there may be relatively shallow water at the seaward approach, where the pre-existing glacier deposited part of its load. Numerous offshore islands, which have become detached from the mainland by submergence, are characteristic of this coastline and the sides of the fjords exhibit many of the features of glaciated mountain valleys described in Chapter 5.

Neutral Shorelines. This type of coast is found where the level of the land and the sea has remained relatively constant over a long period of time. The features are quite varied, and each example is almost a special case, but the most important changes that occur are the result of the introduction of new material in the zone of land and water contact. One of the most common neutral shorelines is that which has been formed by river deltas such as those at the mouths of the Mississippi, Rhine, Nile, and Hwang. The shore itself is frequently flat and may be agriculturally productive but the shallow nature of the river mouth, or mouths, may make contacts between the land and the sea difficult.

Coasts formed by the accumulation of volcanic lava near the sea are a second example of neutral shorelines. Usually they are regular in outline, with only shallow indentations, and have little level land at the water's edge. Their usefulness for man is lessened further by the presence of deep water near the land and a lack of offshore bars or islands. Other neutral shorelines are those formed by faulting and continental coasts bordered by coral reefs.

Compound Shorelines. Coastal zones that exhibit features of both submergence and emergence are classified as compound shorelines, and are probably the most prevalent type. The coast of the eastern United States from the Carolinas to New York belongs in this category, as does that of Southern California. Other examples are found in southern France, western Denmark, and the northern part of the Netherlands.

Along coasts of this type there evidently were several changes in the level of the land and of the sea. Submergence, resulting in the drowning of river mouths and the formation of estuaries and rias, appears to have been followed by emergence and the development of small coastal plains, offshore bars, and lagoons. The central part of the eastern coast of the United States is an interesting example of how man has benefited from events of nature.

Submergence has formed deep and well-protected inlets of the sea which have aided the development of large port cities and slight submergence has provided the offshore bars and lagoons which have become attractive for recreational activities.

SUPPLEMENTARY READING

Bowditch, Nathaniel. *American Practical Navigator*. U.S. Navy Hydrographic Office Publication No. 9. Washington, D.C.: Government Printing Office, 1962.

Carson, Rachel. *The Sea Around Us*. Rev. ed. New York: Oxford University Press, 1961.

Coker, Robert E. *This Great and Wide Sea*. Chapel Hill: University of North Carolina Press, 1947.

King, Cuchlaine A. M. *Introduction to Oceanography*. New York: McGraw-Hill Book Co., Inc., 1963.

Lane, Ferdinand C. *The Mysterious Sea*. Garden City, N.Y.: Doubleday & Co., Inc., 1947.

Ommanney, Francis D. *The Ocean*. 2nd ed. New York: Oxford University Press, 1961.

Sverdrup, H. U.; Johnson, Martin W.; and Fleming, Richard H. *The Oceans: Their Physics, Chemistry, and General Biology*. New York: Prentice-Hall, Inc., 1942.

11

The Fuel Minerals

One of the outstanding characteristics of modern industrial society is its high degree of economic dependence upon mineral resources. Mineral exploitation provides vast amounts of raw materials that are processed in factories and much of the power that is needed to operate industrial machinery. Our present civilization is based in large part upon the metallic minerals which are processed by machines made of metal which may be powered by a mineral fuel, and much of the progress and ease of living that has been achieved by mankind is directly related to advancements that have been made in the use of minerals. Because of the highly uneven distribution of the natural resources of the world, the prosperity and strength of nations is closely related to the availability or unavailability of certain metals and fuels.

Throughout the years that have elapsed since primitive man first began to form bronze from copper and tin to fashion crude tools, the significance of the various mineral deposits has changed as new knowledge has been gained. During the first half of the twentieth century the most essential industrial minerals were thought to be coal, iron, and petroleum. Aluminum and certain other metals are now challenging the supremacy of steel, atomic minerals may soon seriously rival coal and petroleum as sources of power, and it is quite probable that future discoveries will render some now essential deposits obsolete and cause others to become of greater significance to mankind. Since most minerals are exhaustible and irreplaceable natural resources, geographic study of them involves examining the nature, size, and location of deposits, and, in addition, an understanding of what the possibilities are for substituting one for another in case exhaustion occurs.

Although there are many ways of classifying the great variety of mineral resources that are found within the earth's crust, one of the most widely used is a grouping which recognizes three types: the mineral fuels, the metallic minerals, and the nonfuel-nonmetallic minerals. Because of their great complexity and relatively lesser significance the nonfuel-nonmetallic minerals will not be discussed in this volume. This chapter will deal with the mineral fuels (coal, petroleum, and natural gas) and Chapter 12 will describe certain metallic mineral resources.

COAL

Coal, which is buried carbonized plant material, has long been considered to be the world's most important mineral fuel. Recent advances in the use of petroleum, electricity, and atomic energy have detracted somewhat from the significance of coal, but it would still be extremely difficult for a nation to become a major force in world affairs without having access to a large supply of this mineral.

Uses of Coal. The first, and still important, use for coal was as fuel for cooking and heating. Small quantities were mined for this purpose for many years, but it was the development of the steam engine by James Watt in 1769 and the subsequent application of the steam engine to transportation and to manufacturing by machines that was largely responsible for widespread commercial mining of coal. Although electricity has largely replaced the steam engine as a source of power for manufacturing the need for coal has not diminished, for much of the electrical energy used today is generated in coal-burning steam-powered plants. The market for coal was also greatly increased by the discovery of processes by which coke [1] could be combined with other minerals in a blast furnace to produce pig iron, which is the first step in making steel. In the process of producing coke from coal, heat is applied and certain volatile gases are driven off. These gases are captured and become the raw materials for other industries. Many chemicals, drugs, dyes, fertilizers, and plastics are produced from the by-products of the coke ovens.

---

[1] Coke is coal which has had its volatile constituents removed by heating in ovens. It is principally carbon.

Coal Deposits. Although there are many varieties or grades of coal, they all represent the remains of vegetation accumulations that have undergone long periods of hardening and carbonation.

Coal is formed from the plant residues of forested coastal swamps that existed in past geologic times, mostly in the Carboniferous Era of 260 to 285 million years ago. As vegetative matter accumulated to great thickness it was covered by stagnant water and by layers of sand, gravel, or mud. The water prevented complete decay; the weight of the overlying deposits of earth material caused solidification; and as the debris gradually decomposed, oxygen and hydrogen were slowly released and the carbon content of the mass increased. Coal deposits exist as layers in sedimentary rock formations, with seams being interspersed among beds of sandstone, shale, or conglomerate. The arrangement of the strata in which coal beds are usually found indicates that the areas where they occur experienced several periods of subsidence and uplift.

The several grades of coal are classified by their physical properties and by their fixed carbon content. The carbon content is related to the age of the deposit and the degree of change that it has undergone. Although there is a continuous gradation from high to low quality in the grades of coal, the following general varieties are recognized:

Peat is a rather undeveloped form of coal made up of partially decomposed organic matter of a brownish color. It has low heat values and a fixed carbon content of 20 to 25 per cent.

Lignite or brown coal represents the next step after peat in the coal-forming process. It has a carbon content of about 40 per cent, rather large amounts of moisture, and relatively low heating value.

Bituminous or soft coal is black in color, contains 60 to 75 per cent carbon, and has high heating power. Eighty per cent or more of the coal that is mined today is of the bituminous variety.

Anthracite or hard coal has a carbon content of 85 per cent and has very high heating value. It contains little gas and is an almost smokeless fuel.

Graphite, although not a fuel, is almost pure carbon and represents the final stage in the coal-making process.

Conditions Determining the Usefulness of Coal Deposits. Whether or not a known deposit of coal will be mined depends upon the size and quality of the deposit, the geological structures in which it occurs, and its location with respect to markets.

The size and quality of a coal deposit will obviously have great influence upon whether or not it will be exploited. Bituminous coal is the most highly desired type, particularly because it can be made into coke, and if sizeable deposits are available they will be mined in preference to all others. Anthracite does not occur widely and low grade coals may be mined if there is a scarcity of other types. Since coal mining on a large scale requires considerable capital investment, many small deposits of good quality coal remain unexploited.

The type of mining depends upon the rock structures in which the coal seams are located. Some coal layers are situated so near the surface that the mineral can be removed by power shovels in open pits, or *strip mines*. In other instances, the deposits are located in horizontal beds far beneath the surface. Such deposits can be mined only by sinking deep shafts into the earth and extending tunnels outward into the coal layers. In these *shaft and tunnel mines* only relatively thick seams can be exploited economically. Some coal beds which occur as horizontal layers under other rock formations have been exposed by erosion on the sides of valleys, and the coal is obtained from such outcrops through tunnels, or *drift mines*, dug into the valley sides. Any geological disturbance which has resulted in upending, tilting, or bending of originally horizontal coal layers contributed greatly to the expense and difficulty of mining.

The location of a coal field with respect to markets is equally as important as geological structure in determining its usefulness. Some known deposits are situated in the remote parts of continents where mining would be feasible but where costs of transportation preclude exploitation. In regions which do not have high quality coal resources and are located great distances from such deposits, low quality beds or those deposits that have been formed in thin seams may be utilized. The most favorable conditions for coal mining are where thick and horizontal seams of bituminous types are found near the surface and close to large markets.

Major Coal Mining Regions.   Coal is found on all continents but the large deposits of good quality coal are unevenly distributed over the surface of the earth. According to recent estimates, 36 per cent of the coal reserves of the world are found in the United States, 24 per cent in Soviet Russia, 20 per cent in China, and 13 per cent in Europe (not including European Russia). The concentration of the reserves of this major source of fuel and power in a small number of countries leaves many parts of the world with serious deficiencies. The lack of a large and good quality coal supply is particularly critical in Africa and Latin America. Since the demand for coal is not always great in areas with large reserves and because some large deposits are inaccessible, the correlation between producing regions and reserves is not always as close as might be anticipated. Over half of the coal (53 per cent) that was mined in the world in 1963 (Table 2) was produced in four major industrial nations: the Soviet Union, the United States, West Germany, and the United Kingdom. The Soviet Union and the United States between them have 60 per cent of the world's estimated reserves, and both have well-developed manufacturing industries. West Germany and the United Kingdom do not have large coal reserves, but they have long been major producers of coal and possess industries which require large quantities of fuel and power. Many of the other leading producers have become, or are becoming, industrialized and are making maximum use of poor or modest resources.

NORTH AMERICA.   North American coal mining regions are widely scattered and exploit almost all grades of coal. The most productive fields are concentrated in the eastern United States.

The United States has several coal producing regions, but the *Appalachian field,* which produces over 75 per cent of the national output, is by far the most important. The Appalachian field includes the anthracite subregion of northeastern Pennsylvania and a much larger bituminous mining area extending from western Pennsylvania south into Alabama. The anthracite deposits are found in formations that have been folded and faulted, leaving the seams inclined and interrupted; this has greatly increased the expense and difficulty of mining. The bituminous mining areas have large reserves of high quality coal; much of it is suitable for conversion into coke for use by the iron and steel industry. The best deposits are thick and horizontal, and many of them have been exposed on valley sides by stream erosion. The interior field, situated in Illinois and adjacent states, is the second most important producer in the United States and has a large reserve of bituminous quality coal. Some seams are near the surface and can be exploited by strip mining, others require shaft and tunnel operations, and some are so far beneath the surface that they cannot be mined economically at present market prices. The Rocky Mountains, Great Plains, and Pacific Coast regions have small and scattered fields of mostly low quality coal; some of these low quality deposits are mined under adverse conditions to supply the coal consuming industries in the western United States which are located at great distance from the more productive eastern fields. Alaskan coals are thought to be of better quality than those of other fields in western North America, but their remoteness makes their development impractical at the present time.

Table 2

WORLD COAL PRODUCTION, 1963*
(in millions of short tons)

U.S.S.R.	586.1
United States	477.2
West Germany	276.3
United Kingdom	219.3
Poland	141.6
Czechoslovakia	112.0
India	73.7
Japan	57.8
France	55.4
Australia	48.5
South Africa	46.8
Belgium	23.6
World total	2,926.7

* Includes bituminous, anthracite, and lignite.

Data from *Minerals Yearbook 1964*, vol. II, *Mineral Fuels* (U.S. Department of the Interior [Washington, D.C., 1965]).

Canadian coal deposits are limited in area and quality because in a large part of that country the rocks are older than those in which coal is normally found. The best grades of coal are found in New Brunswick and Nova Scotia, where they are mined for use by domestic iron and steel industries.

Mexico has small and scattered reserves of moderate quality coal. The most productive mines are located in the northern part of the country, some 80 miles southwest of Laredo, Texas.

WESTERN AND CENTRAL EUROPE. Western and Central European countries are large producers of coal despite the fact that the resources are modest in both quantity and quality. The high degree of development of coal mining results partly from the heavy demands of industry and partly from the fact that the area is divided politically into numerous countries, each tending toward economic self-sufficiency. Modern attempts toward economic integration in Western Europe, such as the European Coal and Steel Community and the Common Market, may have widespread effects upon coal mining industries.

Coal mining has long been important in Great Britain, but many of the better quality and more accessible deposits have become virtually exhausted. The major mining districts are located on the eastern, western, and southern margins of an upland area known as the Pennine Hills. There is an important industrial district associated with each of the mining areas. Although Britain formerly exported considerable quantities of coal, the amount exported has declined greatly in recent years and coal is now imported at times.

The coal producing areas of continental Europe extend eastward from northern France and Belgium into Poland. Because of the great industrial demands for coal and the political fragmentation of the area, thin seams situated at great depths and low quality grades of coal are often mined. Several fields, located near the borders of two or more countries, have at times been the subject of international controversy. Notable among these are the *Saar Basin* and the district of *Upper Silesia*. Both have substantial deposits of medium to high quality bituminous. The largest producer of high grade coking coal, and probably the most valuable mineral deposit in Europe, is the *Ruhr Valley* of West Germany. Another important mining area is the *Sambre-Meuse* field of northern France and southern Belgium.

U.S.S.R. According to available data, the U.S.S.R., which is credited with having almost a fourth of the coal reserves of the world, is the leading nation in production. The oldest and still most important producing field is the *Donets Basin* of the southern Ukraine. It has large deposits of coking quality bituminous, some anthracite, and is the leading supplier for the industrial cities of European Russia. The second most important field is the relatively new *Kuznetsk Basin* mining district in south central Siberia. Kuznetsk coal was formerly transported to steel plants in the Ural Mountains, but most of the output is now consumed locally. The newer *Karaganda* field, in the Kazakh S.S.R., is third among the Russian coal fields and is now the leading supplier for industrial plants in the Urals. Secondary producing fields are located near Vorkuta in northern European Russia, in the vicinity of Komsomolsk in the Soviet Far East, and in the Moscow area. The latter district produces only lignite and low grade bituminous.

SOUTH AND EAST ASIA. South and East Asian countries, except China, have only small reserves of coal and exploitation is limited to a few areas. Much of the region has never been adequately surveyed for its mineral resources and reliable statistics for production in Communist China are not available.

China undoubtedly has the largest reserves of good quality coal in the Orient, but development of the best fields has been handicapped by their location in remote areas. The government is making a great effort to exploit the coal resources in Shensi and Shansi provinces, to establish manufacturing plants in these areas, and to provide facilities for transporting the coal to other consuming centers. The mines of southern Manchuria have been the heaviest producers in the past and still supply a large part of China's coal. Small mines are also located in the Szechwan Basin and at the base of the Shantung Peninsula.

Japan's coal reserves are small and scattered, the quality is generally not high, and the seams are poorly situated. Despite these handicaps the country is usually one of the world's ten leading producers, for its needs are great. The most important mining areas are in the Sendai district of northern Honshu, the Fukuoka district of northern Kyushu, and on the island of Hokkaido.

India's major coal field is situated in the area near the city of Jamshedpur, some 150 miles west of Calcutta. The development of iron deposits in the region has encouraged the establishment of a steel industry which utilizes a large part of the domestic coal supply. The coal reserves of India are thought to be large in quantity but relatively limited so far as coking grades are concerned.

SOUTHERN HEMISPHERE. The southern hemisphere has small reserves of coal and in the past output has not been great. However, coal mining has greatly increased in Australia and in the Republic of South Africa in recent years and several small fields have been opened in South America. Australia, which probably has the largest reserves in the lands south of the equator, has several mining centers but the largest producers are located on the east coast near Sydney. The most important mines in South Africa lie in a belt which extends north from the port of Durban into southern Rhodesia.

South American coal deposits are limited in quantity and low in grade. Small fields in southern Brazil and in south central Chile are the leading producers but neither country has been able to meet domestic requirements. Recently, mines have been opened near El Turbio in southern Argentina, in the Santa River Valley of coastal Peru, and in the eastern range of the Andes of Colombia.

PETROLEUM AND NATURAL GAS

Most authorities believe that petroleum originated from microscopic organisms that became intermixed with marine deposits which were subsequently buried and subjected to heat and pressure. Like coal, petroleum is found only in sedimentary rocks of intermediate geological age. Accumulations of natural gas are frequently associated with oil-bearing formations. Because petroleum (rock oil) is widely used as a fuel for operating transportation engines and as a lubricant for machinery, it is regarded as one of the three or four most useful and valuable minerals.

Uses of Petroleum. Although historical records show that petroleum was used by the ancients for medicinal and other purposes, the modern petroleum industry originated in the nineteenth century with the search for a satisfactory source of illuminating oil. In the twentieth century, the consumption of gasoline and fuel oil by automobile, ship, and railway engines has far exceeded all other uses for petroleum and has greatly expanded total market demands. Among the most valuable products that petroleum provides are the greases and oils needed to lubricate the moving parts of machinery. Fuel oils and natural gases are widely utilized for heating and cooking, and the petroleum refining industry supplies by-products which serve as raw materials for such other products as asphalt, drugs, medical supplies, paraffin, synthetic rubber, tar, and wax. The energy equivalent of petroleum is greater than that of coal and its utility is enhanced by the fact that it is a liquid which can be transported easily in tanks or by pipelines.

The Occurrence of Petroleum and Natural Gas. Petroleum was probably formed from plant and animal remains that accumulated on the bottoms of shallow seas. Some of this organic material was transported from the land into the seas by ancient streams, and large quantities also originated from microscopic marine life. These accumulations were buried under deposits of earth materials which under heat and pressure became consolidated into sedimentary rocks. Some sedimentary rocks are sufficiently porous to permit oil and gas to saturate the space between particles, others are impervious and form pockets from which the liquid and gaseous substances cannot escape. The rocks must be of the appropriate geologic age, roughly the same as for coal, and four conditions must have been present, before oil can accumulate in sufficiently large quantities to warrant exploitation: (1) there must have been a source of supply for the necessary organic remains to be deposited in oceanic waters; (2) a porous rock layer into which the oil and gas could penetrate, usually sandstone but sometimes limestone, must be present; (3) an impervious layer, such as shale or clay, must overlie the saturated permeable layer to prevent the fluid matter from escaping; and (4) the rock structures must be inclined so that the oil and gas will rise above the water in the saturated layer. The structural pockets in which petroleum is found are commonly formed where the dislocation of horizontal layers has produced anticlines, simple folds, and faults.

Natural gas may be found with oil in solution, it may occur as free gas in the same rock strata, or it may be present in structures which do not contain petroleum. Some 35 per cent of the natural gas produced in the United States comes from oil wells.

Table 3

WORLD PRODUCTION OF CRUDE PETROLEUM, 1963
(in millions of 42-gallon barrels)

United States	2,753
U.S.S.R.	1,504
Venezuela	1,186
Kuwait	705
Saudi Arabia	595
Iran	538
Iraq	423
Canada	258
Algeria	184
Libya	168
Indonesia	165
Mexico	115
Argentina	97
Romania	91
World	9,537

Data from *Minerals Yearbook 1964,* vol. II, *Mineral Fuels.*

Petroleum Producing Regions. The conditions necessary for petroleum to be present in substantial quantities are found only in a relatively small number of places. Recent estimates are that over 60 per cent of the known oil reserves are located in the Middle East (Kuwait has 21 per cent, Saudi Arabia has 17 per cent, and Iran 12 per cent). The United States is credited with 13 to 15 per cent of the total and the Soviet Union with 9 to 10 per cent. Latin America has an estimated 9 per cent, with three-fourths of this amount in Venezuela; and Africa is believed to have 2 to 3 per cent. Asia has very limited oil resources. Europe, with the exception of Romania and Austria, is virtually without reserves. Since the areas with large petroleum resources are limited to such a small portion of the earth's surface, regions having abundant supplies often take on great strategic significance. Industrial nations with heavy demands but inadequate supplies of oil frequently find themselves catering to the whims of underdeveloped countries which have large reserves. There is an even greater discrepancy between reserves and production than was the case for coal. Because many of the nations with large reserves do not have the capital or technical capacity to develop their own resources, the attitude of the government toward permitting foreign participation in oil production is a major factor in determining what the output will be. Of a total world production amounting to 9.5 billion barrels in 1963 (see Table 3), almost one-third originated in the United States, over 23 per cent in the Middle East, 12 per cent in Venezuela, and 15 per cent in the Soviet Union. Within the last few years the output has been increasing rapidly in Canada, Mexico, Argentina, and the Arab state of Qatar.

NORTH AMERICA. North American oil fields extend from western Pennsylvania to southern California and from central Alberta to the Gulf Coast of Mexico. The United States has for many decades been one of the world's largest producers and consumers of petroleum products. The most important Canadian field has only recently been developed, and Mexico is slowly regaining its position as a leading producer.

The United States has become the world's greatest producer of oil despite relatively modest resources. Although estimates of United States reserves have frequently been revised upward over the years, the relationship between supply and demand is nearing a rather critical stage because the imports of petroleum products in some years have exceeded exports. Of the several producing areas in the country the *Mid-continent* (Kansas, Oklahoma, and northern Texas) and *Gulf Coast* (Texas and Louisiana) fields are the most important. Together they have by far the largest proven reserve on the continent and their annual output accounts for over 70 per cent of the United States production. Their output has been rising steadily for several decades but it is generally conceded that the peak has not been reached. Much of this oil moves to major markets by pipeline and there are large shipments by tanker to the eastern seaboard. Three other fields which formerly were leading producers in the United States—*Appalachian, Eastern Interior* (Illinois and Indiana), and *California*—now are relatively less important as suppliers of petroleum products. The yield in the Appalachian area is now only one-third of what it was at the turn of the century; the Eastern Interior and California fields have already passed their peak years of production. The *Rocky Mountain* field consists of numerous small districts scattered throughout a large region. Because of the distances involved in moving the oil to major population centers this field is not well developed. Much of the reserve, however, is owned by the federal government and it is to be expected that it will be of much greater significance as the reserves of other areas decrease.

Although Canadian oil fields are widely distributed, for many years most of the oil for that nation's needs had to be imported. In southwestern Ontario, some wells have yielded small amounts of oil for several decades, and for a time during World War II petroleum was produced in the lower valley of the Mackenzie River in the far northwest. The big change in the status of Canada as an oil producer began when a large field was discovered in Alberta, near Edmonton, in the late 1940's.

Mexico, one of the leading oil-producing nations in the early 1920's, experienced a long period of low output and has only recently regained its position as one of the world's leading producers. After the 1910-1917 revolution, the attitude of the government discouraged expansion of the oil industry and foreign holdings were finally expropriated in 1938. The government agency which took over the industry has lately been able to bring about substantial increases in production, but the output still has not reached the 1921 level of 193 million barrels. The old field near the Gulf Coast city of Tampico is still the leading producer but another district has been brought into operation on the north side of the Isthmus of Tehuantepec.

SOUTH AMERICA. Several South American countries have oil fields but Venezuela has long been the outstanding producer. The reluctance of national governments to permit the technicians and investors of other countries to participate in the search for and exploitation of petroleum has tended to retard development in several nations.

Venezuela rapidly increased its output during the 1920's and since then has been one of three leading suppliers of world markets. The governments have permitted foreign interests to operate on the basis of a 50-50 split of the profits. The oldest and still most important field is located on the northeast side of Lake Maracaibo. In recent years wells have been drilled in the bottom of the lake, in other areas around the shores of the lake, and farther east in the plains and deltas of the Orinoco River.

Colombia has usually been South America's second oil producer but the output has always been far behind that of Venezuela. This is attributable in part to the restrictions that have been placed upon foreign investment in the industry. The major producing area is located near Barrancabermeja, in the lower Magdalena River Valley; smaller fields are located in the Colombian portion of the Maracaibo Basin and in the Caribbean coastal region.

Argentina has a rapidly expanding petroleum industry. The attitude of the government has traditionally been that of economic nationalism and the exclusion of foreigners and, although production was started at Comodoro Rivadavia in 1907, during peak years the yield met only about half of the nation's needs. In 1958 the policy was changed and foreign participation was permitted. New fields have been opened up in Patagonia and at several places along the front of the Andes. By 1962 Argentina was able to supply its own market demands and have a surplus for export.

The petroleum production of the other South American countries is small and of only local significance. A relatively new field has been developed in the Chilean portion of the island of Tierra del Fuego and Ecuador has a small producing area on the Santa Elena Peninsula. Peru has two producing districts; the oldest and most important is near Talara on the north coast and a new, but smaller, producer is located east of the Andes at Ganzo Azul on the Ucayali River. The areas lying to the east of the Andean mountain ranges of South America are regarded as having a high potential for petroleum. In addition to the districts previously mentioned in this zone there are several small fields in southern Bolivia. The Guiana colonies, Guyana, Uruguay, and Paraguay have no known petroleum resources and those of Brazil are very small.

MIDDLE EAST. The Middle Eastern nations not only have a large share of the world's oil reserves but are also outstanding producers. The wealth from oil revenues that has poured into these small and once poverty-stricken countries during the past two or three decades has materially changed the lives of the people and the status of the governments in the world family of nations. The important Middle Eastern oil fields are located on the lowland surrounding the Persian Gulf, on islands in the gulf, and in the lowlands of the Tigris and Euphrates rivers. Some of the oil is shipped out by tanker, large quantities are transported by pipeline to ports at the eastern end of the Mediterranean Sea, and considerable amounts are processed by refineries in the producing countries.

Kuwait, the largest producer in the region, is a small shiekdom not much larger than the state of New Jersey. It is third among the nations of the world in reserves and fourth in production.

Saudi Arabia also ranks high in both production and reserves. The major fields are located in the vicinity of Dhahran and Hofuf, near the Persian Gulf. In addition to the shipments that are made by tanker, Saudi Arabia has a large refinery and a pipeline which reaches the Mediterranean at Sidon in Lebanon.

Iranian oil fields, located near the head of the Persian Gulf, were the first fields in the Middle East to be exploited. Pipelines extend from the producing wells to the port of Abadan, which has what is reputed to be the world's largest refinery. Production has been high in most years but declined radically for a time following nationalization of the industry in 1951. More recently, foreign capital and personnel have been permitted to operate and handsome royalties are received by the government.

Iraq has a large producing field near Kirkuk in the north and a small one near Basra in the south. Much of the output of the former is piped to Mediterranean ports and that of the latter to the Persian Gulf.

Several other political entities in the region produce significant quantities of petroleum each year. The Bahrein Islands are one of the older producers and have become a major refining center. Production on the peninsula of Qatar is of relatively recent origin but that state is now fifth producer among the Middle Eastern nations. Even the Neutral Zone, a seasonal grazing area between Kuwait and Saudi Arabia, has important oil production; the zone is not owned by either country but the two share its oil revenues.

U.S.S.R.   For a long time the major oil fields of the U.S.S.R. were those located in the Baku area on the western shore of the Caspian Sea, and at Grozny and Maykop on the northern slopes of the Caucasus Mountains. Although important refineries are located in each of these fields and Baku is still the nation's leading supplier of petroleum products, the relative importance of these old producers is declining. A new field located east of Kuybyshev, between the Volga River and the Ural Mountains, now produces approximately one-third of the nation's oil, and other important producing areas are located in the Emba River basin, northeast of the Caspian Sea, and in the Pechora River basin in northern European Russia. Minor producing centers are found along the foothills of the mountains of south-central Asia, in the Ukraine, and at the northern end of the island of Sakhalin in the Far East. Petroleum output in the Soviet Union has expanded so rapidly that it now outranks Venezuela and is second only to the United States in production.

SOUTH AND EAST ASIA. The Far Eastern countries supply only about 2 per cent of the world's oil supply each year and are thought to possess about the same proportion of the world's reserves. Indonesia, by far the leading producer in the Orient, has important fields located at Palembang in southern Sumatra, near Medan in northern Sumatra, and near Balikpapan in eastern Borneo. Other producing areas are found in the Irrawaddy River Valley of Burma, in the Brunei colony of northern Borneo, and in the peninsula which makes up the western end of New Guinea. Small quantities of oil have been produced at a few places in China; the shortage of petroleum has been a handicap to the industrial development programs of the communist government, and great efforts are being made to discover new fields, with the prospects being brightest in Sinkiang.

OTHER AREAS. Petroleum producing areas in the rest of the world are few and far between. The Ploesti area of Romania is the only important producer in Europe and several fields have recently been brought into production in the interior of Algeria and in Libya. There are no known oil pools in Africa south of the Sahara or in Australia.

SUPPLEMENTARY READING

Ayres, Eugene. *Energy Sources.* New York: McGraw-Hill Book Co., Inc., 1952.

Bateman, A. M. *Economic Mineral Deposits.* 2nd ed. New York: John Wiley & Sons, Inc., 1950.

Fanning, L. M. (ed.). *Our Oil Resources*. 2nd ed. New York: McGraw-Hill Book Co., Inc., 1950.

Lovering, T. S. *Minerals in World Affairs*. New York: Prentice-Hall, Inc., 1943.

McDivitt, James F. *Minerals and Men*. Baltimore: Johns Hopkins Press, 1965.

Nininger, Robert D. *Minerals for Atomic Energy*. New York: D. Van Nostrand Co., Inc., 1954.

Pratt, Wallace E., and Good, Dorothy. *World Geography of Petroleum*. New York: American Geographical Society and Princeton University Press, 1950.

Voskuil, W. H. *Minerals in World Industry*. New York: McGraw-Hill Book Co., Inc., 1955.

12

The Metallic Minerals

As we learned in Chapter 5, materials of the earth consist of some 92 chemical elements which are combined by nature in a variety of ways to produce a large number of minerals. A portion of the earth's crust which has a concentration of a metallic mineral large enough for the mineral to be mined profitably is called an ore deposit.

THE OCCURRENCE OF METALLIC MINERALS

The ores of metallic minerals are more commonly found in igneous and metamorphic rock structures than in the sedimentary rocks which favor the presence of coal and petroleum (see Chapter 11). Unlike the fuel minerals, concentrations of metallic ores are encouraged by vulcanism and diastrophism. The heat and pressure which accompany tectonic activity cause a molten state in rocks in which the heavier metallic minerals may be separated from the lighter materials. Since the forces which cause metallic minerals to be concentrated in the rocks of the earth are the same as those which cause mountains to be formed, it is not surprising that metallic minerals are more common in highland regions than in plains. In addition, the weathering and erosion processes in mountainous regions tend to expose rock structures and remove loose surface materials and thus facilitate the discovery of existing mineral deposits.

It is not impossible for valuable metallic minerals to be found in sedimentary rocks and in areas with level terrain. Under certain conditions, water seeping through sedimentary structures may bring about the fusion of two or more chemical elements in solution to form a useful mineral. In similar fashion the chemical action of ground water may remove certain minerals and leave

197

behind other more valuable minerals in concentrated deposits. Stream erosion of the rocks of mountainous regions may result in the removal of minerals and their deposition in the valley bottoms of adjacent plains.

THE USEFULNESS OF METALLIC MINERAL DEPOSITS

The fact that a metallic mineral is found in large quantities in a particular locality does not always mean that the deposit will be exploited. The prevailing market price of a metal is a most important factor in determining whether or not a deposit will be worked. The cost of transporting the ore or the refined mineral from the mine to market is another important consideration. Few ores contain metals in their natural state, so the mineral content of the deposit must be taken into account. Obviously, a deposit containing 65 per cent iron will be mined in preference to one containing 30 per cent, providing other conditions are equal. The structural associations under which mineral concentrations are found will greatly affect mining costs, and accumulations which require expensive shafts and tunnels are much less preferred to those which can be exploited from the surface. Other conditions which help determine whether or not a known deposit of a metallic mineral will be mined are the availability of labor and capital and the accessibility of power resources for extracting the mineral from the ore.

IRON ORE

Iron, in the form of steel, is the most important metal man has been able to fashion from the minerals of the earth. The amount of steel utilized by industry each year is several times the total for all other metals combined and the tonnage of iron ore that is mined annually is proportionately large. Deposits of iron ore are widely distributed over the earth, and the processes of extracting the metal from the ore are relatively simple and inexpensive as compared to those for other minerals. Steel has great durability, hardness, and strength, and it can be cast or formed into a variety of shapes. Availability, cheapness, and adaptability, then, make iron the world's most important metallic mineral.

The Ores of Iron. Although traces of iron are found almost everywhere in the earth's crust and iron ores are abundant, the metal seldom occurs in a pure state. Iron exists in many compounds which are mixed in such small quantities with other materials that the expense of separating the usable minerals from the waste does not warrant exploitation. The iron ores that are mined today vary from 30 to 65 per cent iron content, with the less pure deposits being mined only where they are located near smelting plants or can be exploited cheaply.

The principal ores of iron being mined are *hematite, magnetite, limonite,* and *siderite.* The first three are oxides of iron and the fourth is a carbonate. Hematite and magnetite have the highest iron content and are mined in much larger quantities than the other two. The conditions determining the usefulness of metallic mineral deposits, which were described at the beginning of this chapter, are particularly applicable to the ores of iron. Since such large amounts of iron ore are needed each year, deposits that are near the surface and can be cheaply transported to markets are especially prized. Some concentrations are not mined because they contain sizable amounts of phosphorus, sulphur, or other elements which make them difficult to smelt.

Major Iron Ore Producing Districts. Usable deposits of iron ore are widely distributed through the rocks of the earth, and at least 45 countries are engaged in the mining of this mineral. The leading producers are indicated in Table 4, page 200.

NORTH AMERICA. In North America, there are relatively few areas which produce large quantities of iron ore and these are concentrated in the eastern part of the continent. The deposits which yield the greatest amounts of ore each year consist of large reserves of high grade ore which are found near the surface and are situated so that the raw material can be transported cheaply to iron and steel manufacturing centers.

In the United States, for over half a century the Lake Superior ranges have produced the bulk of the ore used by the iron and steel industry. The Mesabi, Vermillion, and Cuyuna ranges of northern Minnesota and the Gogebic, Marquette, and Menominee ranges of the Upper Peninsula of Michigan have high grade iron accumulations which can be moved economically to the shores of Lakes Superior or Michigan for shipment by lake carriers to steel manufacturing centers farther east. Because the famous Mesabi Range has had the largest resource and its deposits

are practically at the surface, in recent times it has produced over
half of the iron ore mined in the United States each year. However, the requirements of two world wars and several decades of
a rapidly expanding economy have exhausted the best deposits
and it is to be expected that the importance of the Mesabi resource will decline steadily in the future. One possible way for
the Mesabi and other Lake Superior ranges to maintain their
production supremacy is through development of economical
ways of utilizing their virtually untouched vast deposits of *taconite*
and other low grade ores.

Table 4

WORLD PRODUCTION OF IRON ORE, 1963
(in millions of long tons)

U.S.S.R.	135.3
United States	73.6
France	57.0
Canada	26.9
Sweden	23.3
United Kingdom	14.9
West Germany	12.7
Venezuela	11.6
Brazil	11.0
Chile	8.4
Peru	6.5
Spain	5.1
World	513.7

Data from *Minerals Yearbook 1964*, vol. I, *Metals and Minerals*
(*Except Fuels*), (U.S. Department of the Interior [Washington,
D.C., 1965]).

The Birmingham, Alabama, district has a much smaller output
than the Lake Superior region, but it ranks second among the
iron ore producing areas of the United States. Some of the ores
are of low quality and most are some distance below the surface,
but the deposit has the special advantage of being located within
30 miles of other raw materials needed for the iron and steel
industry—coking coal, which acts as a fuel, and limestone, which
serves as a fluxing agent to remove impurities. The other iron
mining districts of the United States are widely scattered, their

production is small, and there is considerable fluctuation in annual output. Mines in the northeastern part of the country, particularly in New York and Pennsylvania, produce yields of 5 to 10 per cent of the national total each year. Slightly larger quantities are mined in the western states, with southwestern Utah being the most important producing area.

Canada has greatly increased its iron ore production since World War II. Older producers near the western (Steep Rock) and eastern (Michipicoten) ends of Lake Superior have provided the raw materials for Canadian steel plants for many years in the past. The great expansion is largely accounted for by the new mines in the Schefferville area near the Quebec-Labrador border. Located some 350 miles north of the Gulf of St. Lawrence, the mines exploit a large reserve of high quality ore and utilize the St. Lawrence Seaway to move the ore to lower Great Lakes industrial districts. The mining industry was financed by United States and Canadian interests to gradually reduce dependence upon the Lake Superior ranges as a source of raw materials for the North American steel industry.

In Mexico, the production of iron ore is sufficient to supply the needs of a growing steel industry and in some years small quantities of ore are exported.

SOUTH AMERICA. The South American nations are thought to have large reserves of iron ore. During the past decade, these nations have expanded their production, partly to meet the demands of their own newly established iron and steel plants and partly for greater exports.

Brazil may have a larger reserve of good quality iron ore than any other country in the world. Her increasing steel output, now the largest of any South American nation, has brought an increase in the amount of iron ore that is mined and a gradual expansion in the amount of ore exported. The chief reserves and largest mines are located some 350 miles north of Rio de Janeiro in the state of Minas Gerais.

The Venezuelan iron mining industry, which was not started until the early 1950's, has grown so rapidly that it is now among the world's leading producers. The mines, located in the Guiana highlands just south of the Orinoco River, were established by North American companies to supply ores for steel plants on the eastern coast of the United States. Some of the ore is now being utilized by a new iron and steel complex on the Orinoco River, but most of it is exported to the United States.

Peru's iron mining industry is of even more recent origin than that of Venezuela. The mines, located some 30 miles from the sea in the southern coastal region, were also opened with North American capital and originally all ores were exported to the United States. Peru now has a small iron and steel industry which consumes part of the output.

Chile's iron mines are somewhat older than those of Venezuela and Peru but their development has followed a similar pattern. The major mine, El Tofo, is located a short distance from the Pacific near La Serena in the north central part of the country. At first its production was exported to the United States but now a considerable quantity is used within Chile. The domestic iron and steel industry is somewhat older and larger than those of Peru and Venezuela, and domestic consumption accounts for a larger percentage of the output.

Among the other Latin American iron ore producers, Colombia processes sufficient quantities to supply the needs of a small steel industry, and small quantities have been mined in Cuba from time to time.

WESTERN EUROPE. Although they do not have large iron ore reserves, the countries of Western Europe have large steel industries. For these nations it has been economical to exploit both relatively small and low grade deposits of ore. Small inefficient mines, which have been kept in operation in some countries in the interest of national self-sufficiency, are gradually being eliminated as European economic integration becomes further advanced.

France has the largest iron ore reserve and production in Western Europe. Most of the French ore is located in the Lorraine district on the northeastern border; during the years between the Franco-Prussian War and World War I, the area was developed by German interests. This deposit, which extends into Luxembourg, has an iron content of only 30 to 35 per cent and is high in phosphorus, and its exploitation was not practical until methods for using phosphatic ores were developed in the late 1870's. Although the Lorraine ores are of relatively low quality, their proximity to important coal fields and to the large markets of Western

Europe has made them one of the world's most important sources of the raw material of steel.

Sweden also produces significant quantities of ore for European iron and steel industries. The largest deposits, which have a high iron content, are located at Kiruna in the far north. During the summer months the output of the mines moves south by rail to the Gulf of Bothnia and thence by ship to markets in several countries. In the winter season, when ice closes this route, the ore moves to the sea through the Norwegian port of Narvik. Up to one-fourth of Sweden's annual production is mined in the south central part of the country where it is smelted domestically to produce high grade steel.

The United Kingdom and Western Germany do not have large reserves of iron ore but the demands of their great steel industries have encouraged the exploitation of small and low grade deposits. The most important British mines are located between London and Sheffield and south of Newcastle. The leading West German producing districts are south and east of the Ruhr.

Spain is an important supplier of iron ore for European steel plants and uses some of her production in her own industries. The chief mining district is located on the north coast near Bilbao.

U.S.S.R. The Soviet Union has greatly increased its iron ore production in recent years to meet the needs of its rapidly expanding industrial plant and is now the leading producer of this basic raw material. Since the deposits are widely scattered and the government attitude encourages regional self-sufficiency, a number of important iron mining districts have developed.

Krivoi Rog in the southern Ukraine has ores that are high in iron content, low in harmful impurities, and easily mined. This area is the oldest supplier of iron ore in the U.S.S.R. and in most years is the leader in production. Krivoi Rog ores are utilized in local blast furnaces, in those of the Donets Basin, and in other parts of European Russia.

Magnitogorsk, in the southern Ural Mountains, was not established until after the communist government came into power. Its ores are used principally for steel industries in the Urals. The Kuznetsk Basin, which formerly supplied most of the coal for Magnitogorsk steel factories, has relatively new iron mines which have an output of sufficient volume to supply steel plants in south central Siberia. The Soviet Far East produces sufficient quantities of iron ore to maintain its relatively small iron and steel plants.

SOUTH AND EAST ASIA.   The Far Eastern countries undoubtedly have large iron ore deposits but their size and quality is not well known because the relatively low status of industrial development has not made intensive surveys necessary. India has a large potential production but mining is at present limited to the Jamshedpur area west of Calcutta. China's most important iron mines are found in southern Manchuria and some deposits are being exploited in the lower Yangtze Valley. Although Japan has only small and scattered deposits of low quality iron ore, her industrial demands for the ore are so great that she is one of the largest producers in the Far East. The mines are located in northern Honshu and southwestern Hokkaido. Malaysia and North Korea also produce substantial quantities of iron ore each year.

OTHER AREAS.   Additional iron mining districts are becoming important as Australia, the Near East, and nations in Africa undergo industrial development and as older producing areas are unable to meet the demands of their consumers. The Republic of South Africa, Australia, and Turkey are expanding their iron and steel industries and are able to produce enough iron ore to meet their increased needs. Liberia and Algeria are becoming increasingly important as iron ore exporters and it is expected that Egypt will soon be a producer.

THE FERRO-ALLOYS

Although iron is man's most important metal, it is not particularly useful by itself. It is converted into steel which is made from iron in combination with other elements that are added to give the metal special properties. The minerals which are combined with iron to produce various kinds of steel are called *alloys*. Most alloys are not needed in large quantities but without them much of the usefulness of iron would be lost. Many of the nations of the world which are able to produce large quantities of steel economically are dependent upon other lands for the alloy minerals which give the steel qualities of durability, toughness, resistance to abrasion or rust, heat tolerance, or magnetism.

Manganese.   All steel contains some manganese, on an average thirteen pounds of manganese for every ton of steel. When used in small quantities, the manganese adds to the strength of the steel and larger amounts result in a type of steel with great toughness and resistance to abrasion. Manganese steel is used largely for railroad rails and switches, for mining machinery, and for road working equipment. Of the over sixteen million tons of manganese ore produced in 1963, almost half of the output came from the Soviet Union (Table 5). The most important Soviet mines are located at Nikopol (near Krivoi Rog), at Chiatura in the western Caucasus, and at several places in the Urals. India has manganese mines located in the mineralized zone near Jamshedpur which contains the coal and iron deposits. The most important African ores come from an area north of Kimberley in the Republic of South Africa, but in recent years Gabon, Ghana, the Congo, and Morocco have been increasing their production. Brazil is the newest entry in the field of manganese exportation. In the past its iron mining districts have yielded sufficient quantities of manganese for domestic industries, but the export production comes largely from new mines that have been opened in the state of Amapá, north of the mouth of the Amazon River. The United States produces only small quantities of manganese and is dependent upon overseas sources for its supplies.

Table 5

MAJOR PRODUCERS OF MANGANESE ORE, 1963
(in thousand short tons)

U.S.S.R.	7,345
South Africa	1,442
Brazil	1,383
India	1,185
Gabon	712
Ghana	434
Morocco	369
Congo (Léopoldville)	298
World	16,138

Data from *Minerals Yearbook, 1964,* vol. I, *Metals and Minerals (Except Fuels).*

Chromium. Chromium, which is second among the ferroalloys that are produced each year, contributes to the hardness of steel and helps impart corrosion resistance. It is largely used in steels that are made into tools and machinery which require heat and acid resistance properties. Over 48 per cent of the chromium ore that was mined in 1963 came from South Africa, the Philippines, Southern Rhodesia, and Turkey. Another 31 per cent came from the Soviet Union.

Nickel.   Nickel increases the toughness, strength, and ductility of steel. Like chromium, it also adds resistance to heat, acid, and rust and is widely used in metals for tools and machine parts. The Sudbury district of Canada, near the Great Lakes, produces 60 to 70 per cent of the world's nickel supply. The island of New Caledonia in the South Pacific was formerly considered to be the second leading producer, but the Russian output is now greater. Cuba has mined nickel in commercial quantities at various times and Brazil appears to have considerable resources of this mineral.

Other Ferro-alloys.   Of the many other ferro-alloys that are utilized in steel production, none has an annual total production exceeding 35 thousand metric tons.

Molybdenum increases the strength, ductility, and resistance to shock and is used for stainless, heat resistant, and tool steels. Most of the world supply comes from one small district in Colorado.

Tungsten imparts hardness and toughness at extreme temperatures to steels which are used for high-speed cutting tools. It is estimated that China and the U.S.S.R. produce over half of the world's tungsten each year. Smaller quantities are supplied by Australia, North and South Korea, Portugal, and Bolivia. The United States accounts for 5 to 10 per cent of the world's annual output.

Vanadium adds to the strength, resiliency, and ductility of steel and is used mainly for springs and machinery parts. Much of the world's supply formerly came from Peru, but the leading producers in 1963 were the United States, the Republic of South Africa, and South-West Africa.

Cobalt and silicon are used for magnetic steel; titanium and zirconium for steels that resist change at high temperatures; and boron is a satisfactory substitute for nickel or chromium.

THE NON-FERROUS METALS

In addition to steel, numerous other metals are necessary or desirable for the maintenance of an industrial society. Many of these metals are better for some purposes than is steel, others can readily be substituted for it, and several can be adapted to uses to which steel cannot.

Aluminum. Since World War II, aluminum has gradually replaced copper as mankind's second most important metal. The annual production of aluminum now surpasses that of copper (6.08 million metric tons of aluminum to 5.5 of copper in 1963) and it should be noted that a cubic foot of copper weighs more than three times that of an equal volume of aluminum. Aluminum metal has been available commercially during the present century but its use has steadily increased because of its light weight, strength, resistance to corrosion, and desirability as a conductor of heat and electricity. The growing importance of this metal has been largely the result of technical improvements in production methods which have lowered the price. Steel is still preferred for many structural uses because it is cheaper, but aluminum is a strong competitor of copper in the electrical industry.

The process of producing aluminum involves first the mining of the ore called *bauxite*. The ore is converted into a semi-refined substance known as *alumina,* often near the mines, and finally the alumina is smelted into aluminum bars, ingots, sheets, or wire. This last step requires large amounts of electricity. Bauxite ores are relatively low in aluminum content; on an average 2.2 pounds of bauxite are required to produce one pound of alumina and 1.9 pounds of alumina are needed to produce one pound of aluminum.

Like many other mineral industries, that which supplies bauxite has undergone considerable change in recent years. One of the striking aspects of the aluminum industry today is the discrepancy between the location of the sources of the raw material and the location of the producers of the metal (see Table 6). During World War II the United States, despite its limited reserves, led the world in the mining of bauxite ore. After 1945, production in the United States declined and the lead was taken by British Guiana and Surinam (Dutch Guiana). In 1952 the first bauxite mines were opened in Jamaica and by 1956 that island gained world leadership in production. It had been known since 1942 that Jamaica had large reserves of bauxite but the ores were of such a nature that they could not be processed in existing plants.

Until this time, two types of bauxite were being exploited: the ores of the Americas were a trihydrate type known as *gibbsite* and those ores commonly used in Europe were a monohydrate variety known as *boehmite*. Plants designed for one type of ore could not handle the other type, and the Jamaica ores, a combination of the two types, could not be processed in either; thus exploitation of the Jamaican deposits had to wait until new refineries could be built. According to recent estimates, Jamaica has 19 per cent of the world reserve of bauxite. The other major producers, with the exception of Hungary and Yugoslavia, which together have 22 per cent of the total, have only modest reserves. Ghana and Brazil, which at present have limited production, have 14 and 12 per cent respectively of the world reserve of bauxite.

Table 6

MAJOR PRODUCERS OF BAUXITE ORE, 1963 (in thousand long tons)	MAJOR PRODUCERS OF ALUMINUM, 1963 (in thousand short tons)
Jamaica 6,903	United States 2,313
U.S.S.R. 4,300	U.S.S.R. 1,060
Surinam 3,453	Canada 719
British Guiana 2,342	France 329
France 1,997	Norway 242
United States 1,525	West Germany 230
Guinea 1,638	Japan 247
Hungary 1,340	
Greece 1,261	
Yugoslavia 1,265	
World 30,220	World 6,080

Data from *Minerals Yearbook 1964*, vol. I, *Metals and Minerals (Except Fuels)*.

The major producers of aluminum (Table 6) have access to large amounts of low-cost electricity and are close to major markets. The production figures for Norway and Canada, neither of which has bauxite ores or a large domestic market for the metal, illustrate the significance of inexpensive electricity in the production of aluminum.

Copper. Although copper was one of the first metals known to man, its importance in modern times dates principally from the beginnings of the electrical industry during the last half of the 19th century. The ease with which copper can be drawn into wire, its ductility, and its conductivity of electricity form the basis for its widespread utilization in electrical circuits, but it has many non-electrical uses as well.

Relatively small amounts of native or free copper have been found among the rocks of the earth's crust and most deposits now being exploited are low grade copper sulfides and oxides. Because of the low copper content of the deposits (one to five per cent metal per ton) most mines have processing plants nearby. Processing near the mine involves the mechanical separation of rock particles having a high copper content from the useless materials and the smelting of the concentrated ores into *blister copper*, which is 95 per cent or more pure. Ingots or blocks of blister copper then may be transported to market areas for further refining and use.

Table 7

MAJOR PRODUCERS OF COPPER ORE, 1963
(in thousands of short tons)

United States 1,213
U.S.S.R. 770
Chile 666
Zambia 648
Canada 453
Congo (Léopoldville) 299
Peru 196
Australia 126
World 5,210

Data from *Minerals Yearbook 1964,* vol. I, *Metals and Minerals (Except Fuels).*

The distribution of the world's copper industries is determined by factors other than ore reserves and market demands. Copper once refined is not easily destroyed and can be reclaimed and reused several times. Thus refineries often rely heavily upon scrap copper and are not so dependent upon newly mined ores as are some mineral industries. Since copper is considered a strategic metal, many nations prefer not to be dependent upon supplies from distant sources. For these reasons, as well as the fact that copper compounds are widely distributed among the rocks of the earth, it is not surprising that more than twenty nations produce copper ore and basic metal.

The United States, which is credited with having some 25 per cent of the world's reserves, has for many decades been the leading producer of copper ore and primary metal (Table 7). The first ore deposits to be exploited on a large scale were in the Upper Peninsula of Michigan, but the center of production has since shifted to the mining of low grade deposits in the western states. Arizona, with the largest producers located in Globe and Bisbee, now produces over half of the national output and the mine at Bingham, Utah, supplies another third of the total. Most of the mines are large scale surface exploitation of low grade deposits. Michigan has recently increased production somewhat by establishing operations of this type. The Butte, Montana, mines which at one time produced the bulk of the copper output of the United States are underground operations which yield approximately one-tenth of the total at present; mines near Ely, Nevada, are of some significance. Concentration plants and smelters are located in the mining areas but many of the refineries are now situated on the east coast in New Jersey and New York. Low cost water transportation, nearness to market, and cheap electrical power are the important factors in determining the location of copper refining establishments.

The largest deposits of copper ore outside of the United States are found in the Katanga region of south central Africa where Zambia and the Congo together have another 25 per cent of the estimated world reserve. The ores are of somewhat higher metallic content than those being mined in the United States. Chile's reserve of copper ore is only slightly smaller than that of the Katanga region and for many years the country was the leading exporter of metallic copper. Her position in recent years has been handicapped by distance to consuming markets and by the taxes the government has levied upon the copper industry. In the U.S.S.R., production of copper is concentrated in the Ural Mountains. Canada's copper production is concentrated in the Sudbury district where the ores are associated with those of nickel. The older copper mines of Peru, located in the Andes inland from Lima, have recently been supplemented by new workings in the mountains a short distance from the Pacific Ocean and close to the Bolivian border. Australia's most important mines are located in southern Queensland and on Tasmania. Other important producers not listed in Table 7 are Mexico and Japan. What little ore is available in China is found in the southern interior of the country.

Tin. Tin is another metal that was known to ancient man but was not widely used until relatively recent times. The modern significance of the mineral came after the development of the "tin" can used in the preservation of food and other perishables. The tin can is actually made of thin sheets of steel with a coating of tin; the fine layer of tin serves to make the metal can airtight and prevents rust. Recent developments in the frozen food industry and in packaging with plastics and heavy paper have caused a relative decline in the market demands for tin, but considerable quantities of this mineral are used in the manufacture of bearings, solder, and printing type.

Table 8

MAJOR PRODUCERS OF CONCENTRATES OF TIN, 1963
(in thousands of long tons)

Malaysia	60
China	28
Bolivia	23
U.S.S.R.	20
Thailand	16
Indonesia	13
Nigeria	9
Congo (Léopoldville)	7
World	190

Data from *Minerals Yearbook 1964*, vol. I, *Metals and Minerals (Except Fuels)*.

Approximately two-thirds of the world's tin is produced in southeastern Asia; the remainder comes largely from central Africa and Bolivia (Table 8). Most of the tin ores under exploitation, with the exception of those in Bolivia, are found in the alluvial deposits of stream beds. The most efficient operations are those which utilize huge dredges equipped with buckets and pumps. The tin-yielding gravels are lifted into the dredge where they are subjected to a washing process which removes concentrates of 50 per cent or more metal and discards the waste. Mining methods are most efficient in Malaysia and other areas where large investors have introduced mechanization and less so in China where hand labor is utilized. Except for the output of southern China, Far Eastern tin ores are smelted in Malaysia, Western Europe, and the United States. Communist China has its own smelters. Some tin concentrates from Nigeria and the Congo are refined in Africa but much of the ore is shipped to Western Europe.

Compared with the *placer* or *hydraulic* mines in other regions, tin mining in Bolivia is costly and her share of the world output has been slowly declining. Bolivian ores are located far below the surface where they can be reached only by expensive shafts and tunnels. The Bolivian industry also suffers from a shortage of fuel in the mining area because the ores are low grade and must undergo some concentration to alleviate what would otherwise be prohibitive shipping costs. In addition, excessive charges have been levied on exports by the government. Bolivian tin is smelted in the United States.

Other Non-ferrous Metals. Several of the more important metals not previously mentioned frequently occur together in nature. Lead ores often contain silver and zinc and may include varying quantities of copper, vanadium, antimony, bismuth, and gold. For this reason, a country which is a leading producer of one of these minerals is often important for one or more of the others (Table 9). Lead is malleable, resistant to erosion and many acids, easily alloyed, and inexpensive. Over half of the lead produced is used in storage batteries and as a covering for electrical wires. Zinc is used in galvanizing iron and steel to give protection against oxidation and as an alloy with copper for brass, a metal that is widely used in the machine tool industry. Although considerable quantities of silver go into monetary metal, even larger amounts are needed for other metals, in the chemical industry, and often as a substitute for chromium or nickel. Much of the gold in the world is held in monetary reserves, but considerable quantities are used each year for the manufacture of jewelry, in art work, in the chemical industry, and in dentistry.

Table 9

MAJOR PRODUCERS OF LEAD, ZINC, SILVER, AND GOLD, 1963
(Lead and zinc in thousand short tons;
gold and silver in million troy ounces)

LEAD

Australia	460
U.S.S.R.	390
United States	253
Mexico	209
Canada	199
Peru	163
World	2,805

ZINC

United States	529
Canada	497
U.S.S.R.	450
Australia	394
Mexico	264
Japan	218
Peru	216
World	4,020

SILVER

Mexico	43
Peru	37
United States	35
Canada	30
U.S.S.R.	27
Australia	20
World	250

GOLD

South Africa	27.4
U.S.S.R.	5.1
Canada	4.0
United States	1.5
Australia	1.0
Ghana	0.9
World	44.2

Data from *Minerals Yearbook 1964*, vol. I, *Metals and Minerals (Except Fuels)*.

SUPPLEMENTARY READING

Ayres, Eugene. *Energy Sources.* New York: McGraw-Hill Book Co., Inc., 1952.

Bateman, A. M. *Economic Mineral Deposits.* 2nd ed. New York: John Wiley & Sons, Inc., 1950.

Lovering, T. S. *Minerals in World Affairs.* New York: Prentice-Hall, Inc., 1943.

McDivitt, James F. *Minerals and Men.* Baltimore: Johns Hopkins Press, 1965.

Nininger, Robert D. *Minerals for Atomic Energy.* New York: D. Van Nostrand Co., Inc., 1954.

Voskuil, W. H. *Minerals in World Industry.* New York: McGraw-Hill Book Co., Inc., 1955.

13

Physical Geography in Perspective

Throughout the previous chapters, we have discussed the distribution of the major features of the natural environment over the surface of the earth and the various factors which have caused these features to differ, or to be alike, from place to place. In this final chapter, we shall reiterate some of the concepts that have already been mentioned and introduce others for the purpose of bringing physical geography into closer perspective with the field of geography as a whole. It is not intended that the ideas which follow be all-inclusive, nor are they necessarily arranged in order of importance.

THE INTERACTION OF ENVIRONMENTAL PROCESSES

Although the many agents and processes which cause the natural environment to vary over the surface of the earth have been discussed separately, they are interrelated and seldom does any one of them act independently of the others. The influence of climatic conditions upon other physical elements becomes evident when we recall that the effect of the erosive action of running water in humid lands differs from that in arid areas, and that the soil-forming processes operate differently in the tropics than they do in the polar regions. Several factors acting together have influenced the development of the world vegetation cover. The limits of broad vegetation zones may be fixed on the basis of differences in precipitation; but even under similar moisture conditions, variations in temperature and modifications in soil and slope affect the types of vegetation found within those zones. The factors related to the development of rock structures and terrain containing abundant metallic mineral resources in an area may prevent the formation of fuel minerals in the same locality. The nature of a region's soils may be more strongly influenced by the character of the underlying rock than by climate and natural vegetation. Even the climatic conditions which have such an important influence upon world environmental patterns may be greatly affected by variations in terrain, changes in vegetation cover resulting from human activity, or by man-made structures.

THE REGULARITY OF ENVIRONMENTAL LOCATIONS

Features of the natural environment are distributed over the surface of the earth in a regular and identifiable pattern. One expects to find hot and humid conditions in certain parts of the low latitudes, deserts in specific west coast and interior locations, and coniferous forests in the upper middle latitudes of northern hemisphere land masses. If the continental position and latitudinal location of a place are known, it is possible to predict with some validity the general characteristics of its climate, vegetation, and soils. Although the earth's surface features do not conform to such patterns, the high and rugged mountain systems of the world do have a recognizable pattern of their own. If geographic study is to be more than the mere memorization of facts about places, recognition of this principle of the regular distribution of natural features is one way this goal can be achieved.

ASSOCIATIONS OF ENVIRONMENTAL FEATURES

An important characteristic of physical geography is its emphasis upon associations of features in areas rather than upon individual elements. As we mentioned in Chapter 1, geography may be studied by a systematic or topical approach in which each element of the physical landscape is treated separately, or by a regional approach dealing with portions of the earth that are homogeneous with respect to specified criteria. Although in this book we have used the systematic approach, from time to time the reader's attention has been called to relationships that exist among these elements and to the existence of climatic, landform, vegetation, and soils regions. It would be possible to divide the world into a relatively small number of broad areas or regions in which each area would have closely related conditions of climate, natural vegetation, mature soils, and landforms. The regions so designated would probably have titles such as the humid tropics, the dry lands, the Mediterranean lands, the polar lands, and the monsoon lands. These associations of features, so closely related to world climatic patterns, have been variously designated as *element complexes* or *natural regions.*

A related principle of environmental relationships is that change from one generalized association of features to another usually occurs gradually. Boundaries between deserts and humid lands, between forests and grasslands, and between mountains and plains generally are transition zones of variable width. Lines on maps which indicate these boundaries imply sudden change which seldom occurs in nature.

THE PROBLEM OF GENERALIZATION

Any treatment of world patterns of environmental features is confronted with the rather formidable problem of generalization. No two places on the earth are exactly alike and any broad statement which attempts to categorize areas having similar conditions will almost always have its exceptions. The level of generalization must be appropriate to the purpose for which the generalization is being made. In the case of the world patterns delimited in this book, the reader should understand that there are some areas of level land within mountainous regions, patches of fertile soils may be found in the lateritic belt of the humid tropics, relatively high temperatures do occur within the polar circles, and parts of humid areas will suffer from a lack of moisture from time to time. When general geographic features are represented on a map, the scale limitations of the map may obscure many details but they do not make the generalizations any less valid if the purpose for which the generalizations are made is understood.

MAN AS AN ENVIRONMENTAL AGENT

No discussion of the areal differences and similarities of the earth's physical environment would be complete without mention of the fact that man is an important agent of environmental change. Every portion of the earth that man has occupied has experienced some alteration of the natural landscape. The extent of change is not yet fully understood but the longer the period of occupancy, and the larger the numbers of people involved, the greater the amount of change. Examples of man as an instrument of change are his burning and cutting of forests, destruction of the soil on slopes, draining of swamps, and irrigation of deserts. More recently, his earth-moving equipment has been substantially altering the surface features of areas; and the structures he has erected in urban areas may be causing climatic change. However, our objective in the study of physical geography has been to examine those features which are more the result of nature's forces than of human activity, that is, the earth as it might have been had not man appeared upon the scene.

THE DEVELOPMENT OF NATURAL RESOURCES

Any aspect of the physical environment that man has put to beneficial use is a *natural resource*. Materials available from the earth become resources only when they provide something useful to man. The conversion of some neutral material into a resource is a cultural achievement. An example of this is found in the changing importance of certain rocks and minerals to mankind; today there are widespread demands for aluminum, magnesium, petroleum, and many other minerals which were little known or used less than a century ago. Conversely, many of the materials which were so highly valued by peoples of the past are of minor importance in the modern world.

In a broader sense, any given set of environmental conditions may mean one thing to one group of people and something entirely different to another group. The significance of a particular set of features for the people of a particular culture group may also vary with time. In this sense, it is nature that is regular and predictable and man who is variable and unpredictable. The terrain, climatic conditions, and soils of southeastern China are much like those of the southeastern United States, yet the human use of the two areas is quite different. Even within the confines of a single country the human reaction to similar conditions may be quite varied. Examination of the natural environment of the states of Michigan and Wisconsin would indicate that they are much alike in terms of terrain, climate, soils, natural vegetation, and mineral resources; however, the economies of the two states are quite different. The prairie grasslands of the Argentine pampa and the American Midwest have been put to widespread use only in rather recent historic times. The first Europeans to view both areas found little use for them and it was only after a series of inventions and agricultural techniques were developed that they were to become among the most productive agricultural regions in the world. Nature, then, presents a varying set of opportunities in any area; the way in which men utilize the several possibilities depends upon the attitudes of the people and the level of technology at a given time.

THE TIME FACTOR IN PHYSICAL GEOGRAPHY

In the discussion of the origins of surface features (Chapter 5), it was pointed out that the landforms of any area represent the result of many centuries of interaction between two opposing sets of forces. One set has been at work causing differences in elevation and the other has operated to eliminate variations in relief. Some of these processes such as earthquakes, volcanic eruptions, landslides, and floods are of short duration but most of them effect change by long and slow processes of evolution. The features that exist today represent a stage in the never-ending conflict between the forces of uplift and those of gradation.

The interrelations between temperature, moisture, plants, animals, soils, and terrain have been mentioned many times. Interaction among them in an area may eventually produce a condition of mutual adjustment. A state of equilibrium may exist over an extended period of time but it should not be considered as permanent. Any man-made or natural alteration of one element will result in a series of readjustments in all other elements which will be directed toward another period of equilibrium.

Glossary

absolute humidity. The amount of water vapor that a given volume of air contains, expressed in weight per unit volume.

air mass. A large body of air that has uniform temperature and moisture characteristics.

alluvial fan. An accumulation of sediment laid down by a stream at a location marked by sharp decrease in slope and decline in the velocity of the water.

alluvium. An accumulation of earth material deposited by water.

Antarctic Circle. The parallel of 66½ degrees south of the equator.

anthracite coal. Hard coal having a carbon content of 85 per cent and very high heating power.

anticline. An arch or upfold in a rock structure caused by folding or bending.

anticyclone. A nonviolent storm with a center of high pressure from which winds move spirally outward.

aquifer. A subsurface formation containing a large quantity of water.

Arctic Circle. The parallel of 66½ degrees north of the equator.

arete. A high, narrow, and jagged ridge representing the separation between two cirques in a glaciated mountain region.

artesian well. A drilled or dug opening through which underground water under pressure flows to the surface without pumping.

atmospheric pressure. The weight of the atmosphere at a particular point.

atoll. A circular chain of low coral islands surrounding a shallow lagoon.

bar. A low strip of land paralleling a coastline and separated from it by a shallow lagoon.

barchan. A crescent-shaped sand dune with its two points facing with the prevailing wind direction.

batholith. A huge mass of igneous matter which has pushed outward from the interior of the earth.

benthos. The marine life that grows on the ocean floor.

bituminous coal. Soft black coal containing 60 to 75 per cent carbon, with heating power that is less than anthracite and greater than lignite.

braided stream. A stream having a number of sand bars and islands created by deposition of sediment, and divided by them into a number of channels.

caldera. A large pit or basin at the summit of a volcano, its diameter several times greater than its depth.

chaparral. The low growth of stunted shrubs and bushes found in semiarid areas of California.

chemical weathering. The weathering of rock by chemical processes such as oxidation, carbonation, hydration, and solution.

cirque. A basin excavated by the plucking of glacial ice, found in highland regions and partially surrounded by steep headwalls.

climate. A generalized characterization of the diversified weather conditions of a place over a long period of time.

coal. Buried carbonized plant material that is combustible.

cold front. The zone of contact where polar air pushes into warm air and thrusts it violently upward, causing great atmospheric turbulence.

continental climate. The climate found in the far interior of large continents, particularly in the middle latitudes, characterized by great seasonal variation in temperature.

continental shelf. The terrace-like submerged surface bordering the continents, sloping gently and extending as far as 600 miles out under the sea.

continental slope. The sharp descent from the outer edge of the continental shelf to the great ocean depths.

contour line. A line on a map connecting points having the same elevation.

coral island. A low island formed by the accumulations of the skeletal remains of small sea animals called corals.

coriolis force. The deflective force of earth rotation by which freely moving bodies are deflected to the right of the direction of motion in the northern hemisphere and to the left in the southern hemisphere.

crater. A steep-sided pit or basin, usually at the summit of a volcano, and formed when the top of the volcano was removed by explosion or collapse.

cuesta. A ridge resulting from differential erosion of hard and soft layers of sedimentary rock; it is characterized by a steep escarpment on one side and a gentle slope on the other side.

cyclone. An atmospheric disturbance characterized by winds moving spirally in toward a low pressure center.

deflation. The process by which wind erodes the surface material of one place and deposits the material in another place.

delta. An alluvial deposit formed at the mouth of a flowing stream emptying into the relatively quiet water of a lake, sea, or ocean.

dendritic drainage. A tree-like arrangement of a main stream and successively smaller tributaries joining it at acute angles.

deposition. The laying down in a new location of material that has been carried from another place.

dew. Moisture which accumulates on plants and other objects when, after sunset, the earth rapidly loses sufficient heat to cause the temperature of the atmosphere to drop below the saturation temperature.

dew point. The temperature at which a mass of air becomes saturated with water vapor.

diastrophism. Deformation of the earth's crust by folding, bending, warping, or faulting.

dike. A quantity of magma, or molten material, which has become solidified in a vertical fracture in the earth.

doldrums. An area of calms, variable winds, and low pressure located in the very low latitudes, where the major movement of air is upward.

drumlin. An elongated, half-egg-shaped hill made up of material deposited beneath glacial ice.

dune. An accumulation of windblown sand common in deserts.

edaphic conditions. Characteristics of soil and slope which affect the natural vegetation of areas.

eluviation. The mechanical removal of particles from upper layers of the soil by moving water and the deposition of these particles elsewhere.

epiphyte. A plant which grows upon other plants but does not feed upon them; it receives its nourishment from the air.

equator. An imaginary line circling the earth midway between the poles.

equinox. The time of year when the sun appears directly overhead at the equator; the *vernal equinox* occurs about March 21 and the *autumnal equinox* about September 22.

erg. A broad area covered by undulating deposits of sand.

erosion. The removal or wearing away of the earth's surface by water, moving ice, or wind.

esker. A low winding ridge of sand and gravel deposited by a stream flowing in or under glacial ice.

estuary. A broad, shallow indentation of a coastline where the sea advances far up a river valley, inundating lowlands and permitting tidal currents to back up the river for some distance upstream.

exotic stream. A stream which has its headwater in an area with heavy precipitation, but which crosses arid regions and is usually subject to seasonal flooding.

fault. A fracture in the earth's crust along which movement has taken place.

fjord. A long, narrow, deep, and steep-sided indentation of the sea along a mountainous coast, covering a sunken valley which was formed by glacial erosion.

flood plain. A broad expanse of land in a stream valley which was built up by the deposition of alluvium during the overflow of water.

fog. A mass of small water vapor particles close to the earth, resulting when warm moist air encounters a cool surface or when cool air comes in contact with a warm surface.

fringing reef. A coral accumulation found along the coasts of continents or islands.

front. The line of contact between two unlike air masses.

glacial drift. Material deposited by glaciers.

glacier. An accumulation of ice which has become so large that sufficient pressure is created to cause movement along the outer margins of the mass.

graben. A valley lying between two relatively parallel faults. Also called a *rift valley*.

graphite. A mineral which is almost pure carbon, an advanced stage in the coal-making process.

great circle. A circle which divides the earth into two equal parts; two opposing meridians comprise one great circle, and the equator is a great circle.

Greenwich meridian. *See* prime meridian.

ground moraine. Glacial drift deposited on the ground between other moraines.

ground water. Water which has seeped below the earth's surface and occupies porous spaces in the underlying materials.

ground water table. The top of the saturated zone in which ground water has completely filled the openings between individual soil and rock particles.

hachures. Short lines on a map which represent the slope of the land; heavier lines, or lines drawn close together, indicate steeper slope.

hail. Small ice pellets formed when rain is forced upward into very cold air and freezes.

hanging valley. A tributary valley of a mountain glacier that has not been eroded as deeply as the main trough cut by glacial ice; it is often the site of a waterfall.

hill. A land mass of intermediate elevation having predominantly sloping land.

hook. A curved spit or sand bar projecting into the sea.

horn. A lofty narrow peak located where three or more cirques encroach upon each other.

horse latitudes. Subtropical high pressure belts in the vicinity of 30 degrees of latitude both north and south of the equator.

horst. An elevated area between two relatively parallel faults.

humus. Semidecayed plant and animal matter in soil.

hurricane. A tropical cyclone resulting from excessive heat and humidity of the low latitudes.

hydrologic cycle. The giant circulatory system in which water passes through several stages, from water vapor to precipitation, to surface water, and again to water vapor.

igneous rocks. Rocks formed by the solidification of molten matter.

insolation. The heat or energy the earth receives from the sun.

international date line. The meridian of 180 degrees throughout most of its length, and the line where the calendar advances or loses one day.

jet streams. High velocity winds which move from west to east at high altitudes poleward of subtropical high pressure zones.

jungle. A dense growth of bushes, vines, and shrubs covering the forest floor, typically in tropical areas.

kame. A low, irregularly shaped hill of stratified drift formed under glacial ice.

karst. A type of region having few streams and principally underground drainage, characterized by sink holes and uneven topography caused by the unequal dissolution of underlying porous limestone rock.

kettle hole. A depression marking the place where a large chunk of ice was buried beneath glacial debris and later melted.

laccolith. An intrusive mass of magma which has flowed between layers of sedimentary rocks near the earth's surface and has pushed the overlying strata upward.

latitude. The measurement of position on the earth in degrees north or south from the equator.

lava. Molten rock which flows from fractures in the earth's outer crust out upon the earth's surface.

leaching. The process by which water percolating downward in the soil, or moving across the surface of the soil, chemically removes soluble minerals from one place and deposits them elsewhere.

lignite. A soft brown coal in which the texture of the wood from which it was formed can be seen; it is the next step after peat in the coal-forming process.

loess. An accumulation of fine sand transported and deposited by wind.

longitude. The measurement of position east or west of a line extending from the North Pole to the South Pole and passing through Greenwich, England.

magma. Molten material which moves through the rocks of the earth's outer shell and hardens before it reaches the atmosphere.

mantle rock. The unconsolidated weathered material that has accumulated on the surface of the earth. Also called *regolith*.

map. A graphic representation of all or part of the earth's surface or features.

map projection. Any orderly arrangement of meridians and parallels upon which a map can be drawn.

map scale. The ratio between linear distance on a map and the true measurement of the same distance on the earth.

maqui. A low growth of stunted shrubs and bushes found in lands bordering the Mediterranean Sea.

maritime climate. The climate found along the coasts of the great oceans, characterized by small seasonal variation in temperature.

meander. A winding channel or curve in a slow-moving stream.

meander scar. A dry channel that remains when a slow-moving river shifts course during a time of high water.

mechanical weathering. The weathering of rock by physical forces, without chemical change.

meridian. A line passing from the North Pole to the South Pole, indicating longitude or position east or west of the prime meridian.

metamorphic rock. Rock formed by marked alteration in previously existing rocks and minerals by pressure, by heat, or by the chemical action of running water.

mineral. A natural inorganic substance with fairly definite chemical composition and with distinctive physical characteristics such as crystal form, hardness, color, luster, and manner of fracture.

monadnock. An isolated hillock or ridge on a plain, a remnant of material more resistant to erosion than the surrounding surface.

monsoon. A wind system characterized by great seasonal shifts in wind direction.

moraine. An irregularly shaped hill, or ridges and depressions formed by glacial deposition.

mountain. A land mass reaching comparatively high altitude and having most of its surface in slope.

natural gas. Gas of varying chemical composition frequently found in oil-bearing rock formations.

neap tide. A tide occurring when the line of the earth and sun is at right angles to the line of the earth and moon, every two weeks about the time of the first and last quarters of the moon; little variation between low and high tide.

nekton. A general term applied to the larger fish, shellfish, and sea mammals found in the oceans.

orbit of the earth. The path that the earth follows as it moves around the sun.

outwash plain. A level area formed by deposits of material carried beyond the ice front of a melting glacier by running water.

ox-bow lake. A crescent-shaped body of water formed when a river shifts its channel during high water and cuts off a curve in its course.

parallel. A line circling the earth parallel to the equator, and indicating latitude or position north or south of the equator.

peat. Undeveloped form of coal made up of partially decomposed organic matter.

peneplain. A rolling area which has experienced a long period of erosion during which mountains were gradually worn down to form relatively level terrain.

petroleum. Rock oil originating from microscopic organisms intermixed with marine deposits, subjected to heat and pressure.

plain. An area of low relief and low altitude.

plane of the ecliptic. An imaginary level plane passing through the sun and connecting all points on the earth's orbit.

plankton. Tiny floating plants or feebly swimming or floating animals found in the oceans.

plateau. An area of relatively level land having a higher elevation than a plain and occasionally interrupted by deep valleys and areas of steep slope.

polar easterlies. Winds which originate in the polar high pressure belt and move equatorward, and are deflected by earth rotation to blow from an easterly direction.

prairies. Grasslands in the mid-latitude regions.

precipitation. Water falling from the atmosphere to the earth as a result of the excessive cooling of large amounts of air.

prime meridian. A line extending from the North Pole to the South Pole and passing through Greenwich, England; the line of 0° longitude.

recessional moraine. A deposit of glacial drift laid down during the retreat of a glacier.

reg. Gravelly desert surface remaining after the fine sand has been removed by deflation.

regolith. The weathered material that has accumulated on the surface of the earth. Also called *mantle rock*.

relative humidity. The ratio between the amount of water present in the air and the maximum amount the air can hold at a given temperature.

ria. A sunken river valley where the sea has invaded hilly or mountainous coastline and the interstream areas form bold peninsulas and rugged offshore islands; ria indentations are shorter and shallower than fjords.

rift valley. A valley lying between two relatively parallel faults.

rocks. Aggregates of minerals.

savanna. Tropical grassland.

sea mount. An isolated, steep-sided peak in the ocean depths.

sedimentary rock. Rock formed of particles of solid matter deposited in horizontal layers and later consolidated.

selva. A dense forest of broadleaf evergreen trees.

sill. A horizontal sheet of solidified magma which has worked between layers of stratified rocks.

sink hole. A depression in the earth's surface where water has seeped down and dissolved underlying rocks or collapsed the roofs of caves.

snow. Precipitation resulting from the condensation of water vapor when the temperature is below 32° F.

soil. Unconsolidated material on the earth's surface that is capable of supporting plant life.

soil horizon. A distinctive layer of soil parallel to the earth's surface and having particular chemical and physical properties.

soil profile. A vertical cross-section of the soil horizons or horizontal layers.

soil water. *See* vadose water.

specific humidity. The mass (weight) of water vapor in a unit mass (weight) of air.

spit. A narrow strip of land projecting into the sea, usually at the entrance to a bay or other indentation, and formed by deposition of sand and gravel.

spring tide. A very high or very low tide occurring when the earth, moon, and sun are nearly in line (during the times of the new and the full moon).

stalactite. An icicle-shaped calcium accumulation hanging from the roof of a cave or cavern.

stalagmite. An accumulation of calcium material built up on the floor of a cave or cavern by water dripping from the roof of the cave.

steppe. Short grass type vegetation found on the humid margins of desert regions.

Glossary

storm. An atmospheric disturbance caused by the convergence of two unlike air masses, the excessive heating of a portion of the earth's surface, or by winds being forced to rise over mountain barriers.

striation. A groove made by a glacier indicating the direction of the glacial movement.

syncline. A trough or downfold in a rock structure caused by folding or bending.

taiga. Northern coniferous forest.

tectonic force. A force originating within the earth's interior, resulting from the expansion, contraction, or the transfer of molten matter, involving both the deformation of the earth's crust and the movement of molten material from one place to another.

temperature. The degree of heat or of cold, measured by a thermometer marked in degrees Fahrenheit or Centigrade.

terminal moraine. A deposit of glacial drift marking the farthest advance of a glacier.

thunderstorm. An atmospheric disturbance usually resulting from high temperatures on the earth's surface which cause columns of air to be thrust violently upward.

tidal current. The horizontal movement of water which floods and ebbs, accompanying the rise and fall of the tide.

tide. The periodic rise and fall of oceanic water caused by variations in the gravitational attraction of the sun and moon.

tornado. A violent cyclonic storm of the middle latitudes, especially the midwestern United States.

trade wind. A low-latitude wind blowing from an easterly direction from the horse latitudes toward the doldrums.

trellis drainage. The pattern formed when major streams are arranged in relatively straight parallel lines with tributaries joining them at right angles.

Tropic of Cancer. The parallel of 23½ degrees north of the equator.

Tropic of Capricorn. The parallel of 23½ degrees south of the equator.

tropics. The part of the earth lying between the parallels of 23½ degrees north and 23½ degrees south of the equator.

tundra. A broad area of grasses, bushes, mosses, and stunted trees lying between subarctic forests and polar seas.

vadose water. Water from rain and melted snow which is percolating down from the earth's surface into the ground water table.

vulcanism. The transfer of igneous or molten matter which is frequently accompanied, preceded, or followed by earth movement.

warm front. The zone of contact where warm air rises gradually over a retreating mass of cold air.

weather. The condition of the atmosphere at a place at a particular time, resulting from a combination of the climatic elements of temperature, moisture, atmospheric pressure, and wind.

weathering. The chemical or mechanical breaking up of solid rock into particles small enough to be moved and transported elsewhere.

westerlies. Winds which originate in the horse latitudes, move toward the poles, and are deflected by earth rotation to blow from a westerly direction in both hemispheres.

white frost. Moisture which accumulates on plants and other objects when, after sunset, the earth rapidly loses sufficient heat to cause the temperature of the atmosphere to drop below freezing (32° F.).

wind. Air that moves parallel to the earth's surface.

xerophyte. A plant adapted to a scarcity of moisture or drought conditions.

Index

Italic numbers indicate pages with maps or diagrams.

absolute humidity, 49
Adelaide, Australia, 58, 68
air masses, 40-44, *41*
air movement, influence of land and water distribution upon, 33-34
air pressure, 35, 51
Aitoff projection, 22, *23*
alloys, 204-6
alluvial fans, 93-94
alluvial plains, 114
alluvium, 93
Altiplano, 122
altitude, as climatic element, 48
aluminum, 207-8
Amazon Basin, 60
Anatolian Plateau, 122
animal life, 61 n.
  in arid climates, 66
  in dry summer subtropical climates, 69
  in humid continental climates, cool summer phase, 76
  in humid continental climates, warm summer phase, 75
  in humid subtropical climates, 70-71
  in mid-latitude marine climates, 72-73
  in polar climates, 80
  in rainy tropical climates, 61-62
  in semiarid climates, 67
  in subarctic climates, 78
  in tropical wet and dry climates, 63-64
annuals, 133
Antarctic Circle, 14, 79
Antarctic Ocean, 165, 171
Antarctica, 79, 95
anthracite coal, 182
anticlines, 87
anticyclones, 44, 47
Appalachian Mountains, 107, 110, 119
aquifers, 149
Arab geography, 2
Arabian Desert, 64, 122
archipelago, 175
Arctic Circle, 14, 79
Arctic Ocean, 79, 165, 171
area symbols, 26-27
aretes, 98
arid climates, 64-66
Aristotle, 1, 2
artesian wells, *150*, 151
associations of environmental features, 215-16
Atacama Desert, 64
Atlantic Coastal Plain, 115
Atlantic Ocean, 105, 165, 171
atmosphere, general circulation of, 39-40
atmospheric moisture, 148-49
atmospheric pressure, 35, 51-52
atolls, 176
autumnal equinox, 13 n.

axial inclination, *10*, 11-12
azimuthal projections, 19, *24*, 25
azonal soils, 138, 141

barchan, 99
barometer, 51
Barrow, Alaska, 59, 79
basin flooding, 155-56
batholiths, *90*, 91
bauxite, 207-8
benthos, 167, 168
Bergen, Norway, 59, 72
biological factors in soil formation,
    139
bituminous coal, 182, 183
black prairie soils, 142-43
blister copper, 209
block diagrams, 27
block fault mountains, 107
blowouts, 99
boehmite, 208
Bogota, Colombia, 59, 81
Bonne projection, 21, *22*
boreal forest, 131
boreal forest climate, 77
braided stream, 153
broadleaf forests, 130-31
Broome, Australia, 58
Bucharest, Romania, 59, 74
Buenos Aires, Argentina, 59, 69
bunch grass, 130, 133

calderas, 107
campos, 62
carbonation in weathering, 91
Carboniferous Era, 182
cartograms, 29
Cauca Valley of Colombia, 161
Central Valley of California, 161
centrifugal force, 10
chaparral, 130
chemical composition of oceanic
    waters, 165

chemical elements in the earth's
    crust, 85
chemical weathering, 91-92
chernozems, 143
chestnut brown soils, 143
chromium, 205-6
cirques, 98
clay, 137
climate, 30
climatic controls, 30-49
climatic data for representative
    stations, 58-59
climatic elements, 49-52
climatic types, 54-83, *56*
clouds, 50-51
coal, 181-88
coal mining regions, 184-88
    Africa, 188
    Asia, South and East, 187-88
    Australia, 188
    Europe, Western and Central,
        186
    North America, 184-86
    South America, 188
    U. S. S. R., 186-87
coastal plains, 112
cobalt, 206
coke, 181 n.
cold front, *46*, 47
Colorado Plateau, 122
Columbia Plateau, 122
Columbus, Ohio, 59, 74
compound shorelines, 178-79
condensation, 49-50
conformal projections, 19
Congo Basin, 60
conic projection, *21*
coniferous forest, 131
continental climate, 34-35
continental glaciers, 95, *96*
continental islands, 175
continental plateaus, 121
continental shelf, 173
continental slope, 173
contour lines, *26*, 27

convective precipitation, 51
convective thunderstorms, *43*, 44
copper, 208-211
coral islands, 174, 176
coral reefs, 178
corals, 176
core of the earth, 84
coriolis force, 37 n.
Corn Belt of the United States, 73, 143
Crater Lake, Oregon, 107
craters, 107
crust of the earth, 84-85
  chemical elements in, 85
cuestas, 107
Cuiabá, Brazil, 58, 62
culture, 5, 6, 217
cyclones, 44-47, *45*
cylindrical projections, 19, *20*

Danubian Plain, 74
Darjeeling, India, 59, 81, 82
Dawson, Canada, 59, 77
Deccan Plateau, 122
deciduous forest, 129, 131
deductive method, 5
deflation, 99
deltas, *94*, 95, 114, 178
dendritic drainage, 119, 153
Denver, Colorado, 58, 66
deposition, 92-95
depositional plains, 114-15
desert soils, 143-44
desert vegetation, 65-66
deserts, 64-67, 133-34
dew, 50
dew point, 49-50
diastrophism, 86-91, 197
dike, 90
dissected plateau, *121*
doldrum belt, 36
dome volcanoes, 109
domed mountains, 107
dot maps, 28

drainage patterns, 153
drift mines, 183
drift of ocean waters, 47-48
drift plains, 115
drumlins, 97
dry summer subtropical climate, 67-69
dunes, 99

earth, 8-29
  area of, 8
  axial inclination, 11-12, 32
  axial parallelism, 11-12, 32
  coordinates, *13*
  internal structure of, 84-85
  materials, 84-86
  orbit of, *10*
  revolution, 9-10, 32
  rotation, 10, 32, 47-48
  size and shape of, 8
earth grid, 12
earth-sun relationships, 8-12, *11*
earthquakes, 89
edaphic conditions, 127-28
element complexes, 216
elevation, 48, 80-81, 105, 134
elliptical projections, 22, *23*
eluviation, 138-39
environmental determinism, 3
epiphytes, 129
equal-area projections, 19
equator, 12-13
equatorial low pressure belt, 36
equinoxes, 13 n.
erg, 100
eroded hills, *118*
erosion, 92-101
  by glaciers, 95-99, 177-78
  by ocean waves and currents, 100-1, 176-77
  by running water, 92-93
  by subsurface water, 100
  by wind, 99-100
erosional plains, 113

eskers, 97
estuaries, 171, 177
European Coal and Steel Community, 186
European Common Market, 186
evergreen forests, 129
exotic streams, 152
extrusive vulcanism, 89-90

fault, 89
faulted mountains, *105*, 106
faulting, *88*, 89, 178
fauna, 61 n.
ferro-alloys, 204-6
Finch, V. C., 22, 25
fjords, 177-78
flood plains, 93, 114
fog, 50
folded mountains, *105*, 107
folding, 87-89, *87*
forests, 128-31
fringing reefs, 176
front, 41, *46*
frontal precipitation, 51
fuel minerals, 180-96

gallery forest, 63, 132
geographic methods of investigation, 5-6
    regional approach, 5, 215-16
    systematic approach, 5, 7, 215
geographic principle, 6
geography, 1-7
    definitions of, 3-4
    functions of, 6
    historical background, 1-3
gibbsite, 208
glacial drift, 97
glaciated hills, 119
glaciated mountains, *98*, 99
glaciers, 95-99
glacio-lacustrine plains, 98
gnomonic projection, *24*, 25
Gobi Desert, 64

gold, 212-13
Goode, J. Paul, 25
graben, 107
Grand Banks, 168
graphic scale, 18
graphite, 182
grasslands, 131-33
gravity, 9, 170
gravity waves, 169
gray brown podsols, 142
Great Basin, 64
great circles, 12
Great Plains of North America, 115
Great Sandy Desert, 64
great soil groups, 141
Great Valley of California, 68
Great Victoria Desert, 64
Greek geographers, 1-2
Greenwich meridian, 15
ground moraines, 97
ground water, 100, 149
ground water table, 100, 149
Gulf Coastal Plain, 115

hachures, *26*, *27*
hail, 50
hanging valleys, 99
hardpan, 139
hematite, 199
high islands, 175
highland climates, 80-83
highland vegetation, 134
hills, *104*, 117-120, *118*
hooks, 101
horns, 98
horse latitudes, 36-37
horsts, 107
humid continental climates, cool summer phase, 75-76
humid continental climates, warm summer phase, 73
humid subtropical climates, 69-71
humidity, 49-50
humus, 137, 139
hurricanes, 47

hydration in weathering, 91
hydraulic mines, 212
hydroelectric power, 157-58
hydrologic cycle, *147*, 148
hypotheses, 6

ice, 50
ice scour, 97
icecap climate, 79
igneous rocks, 85-86
    metallic mineral deposits in, 197
Indian Ocean, 165, 174, 175
inductive method, 5
insolation, *31, 32*
interaction of environmental pro-
        cesses, 214-15
interior of the earth, 84
interior plains, 112
intermittent streams, 152
intermontane basins, 122
intermontane plateaus, 121
international date line, 15
interrupted projections, 22, 25
intrazonal soils, 141
intrusive vulcanism, 90-91
Iquitos, Peru, 58, 60, 81
Iranian Plateau, 122
iron ore, 198-99
iron producing areas, 199-204
    Africa, 204
    Asia, South and East, 204
    Australia, 204
    Europe, Western, 202-3
    North America, 199-201
    South America, 201-2
    U. S. S. R., 203-4
irrigation, 155-56
isarithm, 27
island chain, 175
islands, 175-76
isobars, 27
isohyets, 27-28
isopleths, 27, 28
isotherms, 27, *34*

jet streams, 40
jungle, 61, 129

Kalahari Desert, 64
kames, 97
Kano, Nigeria, 58, 62
karst, 100, *113*, 114, 115
kettle holes, 97
Khartoum, Sudan, 58, 65
Köppen, Wladimir, 54
Köppen system, 54-55, 57

laccoliths, *90*, 91, 107
lacustrine plains, 112, 114-15
land bridges, 175
land and water distribution, effect
        on climate, 33-35
landform types, 103-23, *104, 108*
    classification, 103-5
    hills, 104, 117-20, *118*
    mountains, 103-4, *105*, 105-11
    plains, 104, 111-17, *112, 113*
    plateaus, 104, 120-23, *121*
latent heat of condensation, 44 n.
latent heat of vaporization, 44 n.
laterites, 141
latitude, 12-14
    as climatic control, 31-33
    in place location, 15
lava, 89, *90*, 122, 178
leaching, 138
lead, 212, 213
leeward slopes, 49
legal aspects of water use, 161-63
lignite, 182
limonite, 199
line symbols, 27
llanos, 62
local relief in landform classifica-
        tion, 103
    hills, 117
    plains, 111-12
    plateaus, 120

location of places, 12-16
loess, 100, 116, 119
longitude, 14-15, 17
Los Angeles, California, 58, 68
low islands, 175, 176

magma, 90
magnetite, 199
man as an environmental agent, 216-17
manganese, 204-5
mantle rock, 92
map projections, 19-25
    Aitoff, 22, *23*, 25
    azimuthal, 19, *24*, 25
    Bonne, 21, *22*
    conic, *21*
    elliptical, 22, *23*
    gnomonic, *24*, 25
    interrupted, 22, 25
    Mercator, 19, *20*, 21
    Mollweide, 22, *23*, 25
    orthographic, *24*, 25
    polyconic, 21, *41*
    rectangular, 19, *20*, 21
    sinusoidal, 22, *23*
    stereographic, *24*, 25
map scales, 17-18
map symbols, 26-29
maps, 17-29
maqui, 130
margins of the oceans, 176-77
Marianas Trench, 174
marine life, 167-69
maritime climates, 34-35
mature mountains, 106
mature soils, 139-41
mean temperatures, *34*
meanders, 114
mechanical weathering, 92
Mediterranean climates, 67-69
Mediterranean scrub forest, 130
Mediterranean Sea, 68, 69, 130
Mercator projection, 19, *20*, 21

meridians, 12, 15
metallic minerals, 197-213
metamorphic rocks, 86
    metallic mineral deposits in, 197
Mexican Plateau, 64
Mexico City, 59, 81
Mid-Atlantic Ridge, 174, 175
mid-latitude marine climates, 71-73
Middle Ages, 2
minerals, 85
    fuel, 180-95
    metallic, 197-213
mines, 183, 198, 211-12
Missouri Valley, 161
mixed broadleaf-coniferous forest, 131
modern geography, 3-5
Mollweide projection, 22, *23*, 25
molybdenum, 206
monadnocks, 113
monsoon rainforest, 129
monsoons, 38-39, 40, 60, 70, 82
Montgomery, Alabama, 58, 69
moon, 169-70
moraines, *96*, 97-98, 115
Moscow, U. S. S. R., 59, 75
mountain barriers, 48-49
mountain climates, 80-83
mountain glaciers, 95, *98*, 99
mountain systems, 81, 109-10
mountains, 103, *104*, 105-111
    block fault, 107
    distribution of, 109-10
    domed, 107
    faulted, *105*, 106-7
    folded, 107
    mature, 106
    old, 106
    submarine, 173-74
    types, 106-9
    volcanic, 107
    young or youthful, 106
multiple use water projects, 159-61
Murray-Darling Valley, 161
Muslim geographers, 2

natural gas, 188, 189
natural levees, 93
natural regions, 216
natural resources, 217-18
neap tide, 170
nekton, 167, 168
neutral shorelines, 178
nickel, 206
non-consuming water uses, 156-59
non-ferrous metals, 206-13
normal fault, 88, 107
northern coniferous forest, 131

oceanic whirls, 39, 40
oceans, 164-79
  area of, 165
  chemical composition of water, 165-66
  color of water, 166
  continental shelf, 173
  continental slope, 173
  currents, 47-48, 100-1, 170-73, *172*
  floor, 173-75
  marine life, 167-69
  plains, 174-75
  pressure, 166
  shorelines, 100-1, 176-78
  submarine mountains, 173-74
  temperature of water, 166
  tidal currents, 170
  tides, 169-70
  trenches, 174
  waves, 169
  world ocean, 164-65
offshore bars, 101, 176-77
oil, *see* petroleum
old mountains, 106
orographic precipitation, 51
orographic thunderstorms, *43*, 44
orthographic projection, *24*, *25*
outwash plains, *96*, 98, 115
ox-bow lakes, 114
oxidation in weathering, 91

Pacific Ocean, 165, 171, 174, 175
pampa, 116, 133, 143
parallelism, *10*, 11-12
parallels, 12-14
Paraná Plateau, 122
parasites, 129
parent material, 92, 136, 138
Patagonian Desert, 64
Patagonian Plateau, 121
peat, 182
peneplains, 113
perennials, 133
Persian Gulf, 166
petroleum, 188-95
petroleum producing regions, 190-95
  Asia, South and East, 195
  Europe, 195
  Middle East, 193-94
  North Africa, 195
  North America, 191-92
  South America, 192-93
  U. S. S. R., 194-95
photosynthesis, 127, 167 n.
physical geography, 6-7
  in perspective, 214-18
phytoplankton, 167
piedmont plains, 112, 115
piedmont plateaus, 121
place location, 12-16
placer mines, 212
plains, *104*, 111-117
  alluvial, 114
  coastal, *112*
  delta, 114
  depositional, 114-15
  distribution of, 115-16
  drift, 115
  erosional, 113
  flood, 93, 114
  glacio-lacustrine, 98
  interior, 112
  karst, *113*, 114
  lacustrine, 112, 114-15
  loess, 116

plains—*continued*
    oceanic, 174-75
    outwash, 98, 115
    piedmont, 112, 115
    till, 115
    utilization of, 116-17
plane of the ecliptic, 10, 11
planets, 8
plankton, 167-68
plant associations, 128
plant growth, 125-28
plastic shading, 27, *28*
plateaus, *104*, 120-23, *121*
    distribution of, 122
    types of, 121-22
    utilization of, 122-23
podsols, 142
polar climates, 78-80
polar continental air masses, 42
polar continental climate, 77
polar easterlies, 37
polar fronts, 38
polar high pressure zones, 37
polar marine climate, 78
polar maritime air masses, 42
polar outbursts, 40
polyconic projection, 21, *41*
prairies, 132-33
precipitation
    in arid climates, 65
    causes of, 51
    as climatic element, 49-51
    convectional, 51
    in dry summer subtropical
        climates, 68
    effect on vegetation, 127
    frontal, 51
    in highland climates, 81-82
    in humid continental climates,
        cool summer phase, 76
    in humid continental climates,
        warm summer phase, 74
    in humid subtropical climates, 70
    measurement of, 51

    in mid-latitude marine climates,
        72
    orographic, 51
    in polar climates, 79
    in rainy tropical climates, 60
    in semiarid climates, 67
    in subarctic climates, 77
    in tropical wet and dry climates,
        63
precipitation effectiveness, 127
pressure, air, 51-52
pressure and winds, 35-40
pressure of oceanic water, 166
prime meridian, 15
priority rights (to water), 162
Ptolemy, 2
Puerto Montt, Chile, 59, 72

radial drainage patterns, 153
rain, 50-51
rain shadow, 49
rainy tropical climates, 57, 60-62
Rangoon, Burma, 58, 60
recessional moraines, 97
rectangular projections, 19-21, *20*
red and yellow laterites, 141-42
reefs, fringing, 176
reg, 99
region, 5, 215-16
regional geography, 5
regolith, 92, 136
regularity of environmental loca-
        tion, 215
relative humidity, 49 n., 50
relief, 103, *104*
Renaissance geography, 3
revolution of the earth, 9-10, 32
Rhone Valley, 161
rias, 177
rift valley, 107
riparian rights, 162
rocks, 85-86
    igneous, 85-86, 197
    metamorphic, 86, 197

sedimentary, 86, 182, 188, 189, 197
Roman geographers, 2
rotation of the earth, 10, 32, 47-48
running water, erosion and deposition by, 92-95
runoff, 151

Sahara Desert, 64, 122
St. Paul, Minnesota, 59, 75
sand, 137
sand bars, 176-77
sand dunes, 119
Santa Cruz, Argentina, 58
São Francisco Valley of Brazil, 161
savanna, 62, 63, 132
sea, definition of, 164-65
sea mounts, 174
seas, *see* oceans
seasons, *14*
Seattle, Washington, 72
sedimentary rocks, 86, 197
    fuel mineral deposits in, 182, 188, 189
    metallic mineral deposits in, 197-98
selva, 61, 128
semiarid climates, 66-67
shaft and tunnel mines, 183
shield volcanoes, 109
shorelines, 176-79
    compound, 178-79
    effect of waves and currents on, 100-1
    of emergence, 176-77
    neutral, 178
    of submergence, 177-78
siderite, 199
silicon, 206
sills, 90
silt, 137
silver, 212-13
sink holes, 100
sinusoidal projection, 22, *23*

snow, 50-51
soil water, 149
soils, 136-144, *140*
    in arid climates, 66
    azonal, 138
    biological factors in, 139
    characteristics of, 136-38
    chernozems, 143
    chestnut brown soils, 143
    color, 137-38
    desert, 143-44
    in dry summer subtropical climates, 69
    formation of, 138-39
    horizons, 136-37
    in humid continental climates, cool summer phase, 76
    in humid continental climates, warm summer phase, 75
    in humid subtropical climates, 71
    laterites, 141-42
    leaching of, 138
    mature soils, 139-41
    in mid-latitude marine climates, 73
    mountain, 144
    pan layer in, 139
    parent material, 136, 138
    podsols, 142
    polar climates, 80
    prairie, 142-43
    profile, 136-37
    in rainy tropical climates, 62
    in semiarid climates, 67
    structure, 137
    in subarctic climates, 78
    texture, 137
    in tropical wet and dry climates, 64
    tundra, 144
solar energy, 31-33
solar system, 8, *9*
solution in weathering, 91
Sonoran Desert, 64

soroche, 52
source regions, 41
specific humidity, 49 n.
spits, 101
spring tide, 170
springs, 151
stalactites, 100
stalagmites, 100
steppe, 67, 133
stereographic projection, *24*, 25
storms, 40, 42-47
Strabo, 2
stream patterns, 153
streams, 151-53
striations, glacial, 97
strip mines, 183
structural hills, 119
subarctic climates, 76-78
submarine mountains, 173-74
subpolar low pressure belts, 38
subsurface water, 100
subtropical high pressure belts, 36-37
sun, 8-12
sunlight, effect on vegetation, 127
surface water, 151-53
Svalbard, 59, 79
synclines, 87
systematic geography, 5

tablelands, 104
taconite, 200
taiga, 78, 131
tectonic forces, 86-91
temperate marine climate, 71-73
temperature
  air, 31-33, 49
  in arid climates, 65
  average monthly, 60 n.
  as climatic element, 49
  in dry summer subtropical climates, 68
  effects on vegetation, 126-27
  in highland climates, 81

in humid continental climates, cool summer phase, 75-76
in humid continental climates, warm summer phase, 74
in humid subtropical climates, 69-70
influence of land and water distribution upon, 33
influence of latitude upon, 31-33
mean daily temperature, 60 n.
in mid-latitude marine climates, 71-72
of oceanic waters, 166
in polar climates, 79
in rainy tropical climates, 60
in semiarid climates, 66
in subarctic climates, 77
in tropical wet and dry climates, 62-63
Tennessee Valley Authority, 160-61
terminal moraines, 97
Thar Desert, 64
theory, 6
Thornthwaite, C. Warren, 54
thrust fault, 88
thunderstorms, *43*, 44
tidal currents, 170
tides, 169-71
tierra caliente, 82, 110, 134
tierra fria, 82, 110, 134
tierra templada, 82, 110, 134
till plains, 115
time factor in physical geography, 218
time zones, *16*, 17
tin, 211-12
titanium, 206
topographic maps, 27
tornadoes, 47
trade wind belts, 37
trellis drainage, 119, 153
trenches, oceanic, 174
Tropic of Cancer, 13-14, 32
Tropic of Capricorn, 13-14, 32
tropical continental air masses, 42

tropical maritime air masses, 42
tropical rainforests, 128-29
tropical scrub and thorn forest, 129-30
tropical semideciduous forest, 129
tropical wet and dry climate, 62-64
true direction maps, 19
true shape maps, 19
tundra, 80, 133-34, 144
tungsten, 206

underground water, 149-51
undifferentiated highlands, 80

vadose water, 149
valley glaciers, 95, 98-99
vanadium, 206
vegetation, 125-35, *126*
    in arid climates, 65-66
    conditions affecting growth, 125-28
    desert, 133-34
    in dry summer subtropical climates, 68-69
    forests, 128-31
    grasslands, 131-33
    highland, 134
    in highland climates, 82-83
    in humid continental climates, cool summer phase, 76
    in humid continental climates, warm summer phase, 74-75
    in humid subtropical climates, 70
    in mid-latitude marine climates, 72
    plant associations, 128
    in polar climates, 80
    in rainy tropical climates, 61
    in semiarid climates, 67
    in subarctic climates, 78
    in tropical wet and dry climates, 63
vertical zonation, 82-83, 110

veld, 62
verbal scale, 18
vernal equinox, 13 n.
volcanic islands, 175
volcanic mountains, *90*, 107-9
volcanoes, *90*, 107-9
vulcanism, 87, *88*, 89-91, 197

warm front, *46*, 47
warping, 89
water, 146-63
    consumption, 153-56
    cycle, *147*, 148
    forms of, 147
    importance of, 146-47
    multiple-use water projects, 159-61
    non-consuming water uses, 156-59
    for recreation, 159
    supply, 147-53, 154-55
    surface water, 151-53
    for transportation, 158-59
    underground, 149-51
    use in irrigation, 155-56
    water-consuming activities, 153-56
water power, 157-58
water resources, 146-63
water rights, 161-63
water table, 100
wave built terraces, 101
wave cut cliffs, 101
wave cut terraces, 101
waves, 169
    erosion and deposition by, 100-1
weather, 30
weathering, 91-92
wells, 149-51, 156
west coast marine climate, 71-73
westerly wind belts, 37
white frost, 50
wind and pressure belts, 35-40, *36*
    modifications of, 38-39

wind erosion, 99-100
winds, 33, 35-40, *39*, 52
    as climatic controls, 35-40
    as climatic element, 52
    effect of latitude upon, 33
    erosion by, 99-100
windward slopes, 48-49
world ocean, 164-65

xerophytic plants, 130, 133

Yakutsk, U. S. S. R., 59, 77
young mountains, 106
Yucatan Peninsula, 115

zinc, 212-13
zonal soils, 141
zooplankton, 167